Contents

Introduction

1

Quick Start

2

P9-BIA-607

How Simulink Works

3

RELEASE 13

Learning
SIMULINK® 5

MATLAB®
STUDENT VERSION
with SIMULINK®

The MathWorks

How to Contact The MathWorks:

| www.mathworks.com | Web |
| comp.soft-sys.matlab | Newsgroup |

suggest@mathworks.com	Product enhancement suggestions
bugs@mathworks.com	Bug reports
doc@mathworks.com	Documentation error reports

ISBN 0-9672195-8-2

Learning Simulink

Printing History:	August 1999	First printing	New manual
	January 2001	Second printing	Revised for Simulink 4.0 (Release 12)
	November 2002	Third printing	Revised for Simulink 5.0 (Release 13)

Simulink Basics

4

Creating a Model

5

Working with Blocks

6

Working with Signals

7

Running a Simulation

8

Analyzing Simulation Results

9

Creating Masked Subsystems

10

Block Libraries

Introduction

This chapter introduces the MATLAB Student Version and provides resources for using it.

About the Student Version (p. 1-2)	Description of the Student Version and how it differs from the professional version.
Obtaining Additional MathWorks Products (p. 1-6)	How to acquire other products that work with the Student Version.
Getting Started with Simulink (p. 1-7)	Steps for learning how to use Simulink.
Finding Reference Information (p. 1-8)	Techniques for learning more about Simulink.
Troubleshooting and Other Resources (p. 1-9)	Additional sources of information for the Student Version products.
About Simulink (p. 1-13)	High-level description of Simulink.

About the Student Version

MATLAB® and Simulink® are premier software packages for technical computation in education and industry. The MATLAB Student Version provides all of the features of professional MATLAB, with no limitations, and the full functionality of professional Simulink, with model sizes up to 300 blocks. The Student Version gives you immediate access to the high-performance numeric computing, modeling, and simulation power you need.

MATLAB allows you to focus on your course work and applications rather than on programming details. It enables you to solve many numerical problems in a fraction of the time it would take you to write a program in a lower level language. MATLAB helps you better understand and apply concepts in applications ranging from engineering and mathematics to chemistry, biology, and economics.

Simulink, included with the Student Version, is a block diagram tool for modeling and simulating dynamic systems, including controls, signal processing, communications, and other complex systems.

The Symbolic Math Toolbox, also included with the Student Version, is based on the Maple® 8 symbolic kernel and lets you perform symbolic computations and variable-precision arithmetic.

MATLAB products are used in a broad range of industries, including automotive, aerospace, electronics, environmental, telecommunications, computer peripherals, finance, and medical. More than 500,000 technical professionals at the world's most innovative technology companies, government research labs, financial institutions, and at more than 2,000 universities, rely on MATLAB and Simulink as the fundamental tools for their engineering and scientific work.

Student Use Policy

This Student License is for use in conjunction with courses offered at a degree-granting institution. The MathWorks offers this license as a special service to the student community and asks your help in seeing that its terms are not abused.

To use this Student License, you must be a student using the software in conjunction with courses offered at degree-granting institutions.

You may not use this Student License at a company or government lab. Also, you may not use it for research or for commercial or industrial purposes. In these cases, you can acquire the appropriate professional or academic version of the software by contacting The MathWorks.

Differences Between the Student Version and the Professional Version

MATLAB

The MATLAB Student Version provides full support for all language features as well as graphics, external interface and Application Program Interface (API) support, and access to every other feature of the professional version of MATLAB.

MATLAB Differences. There are a few small differences between the Student Version and the professional version of MATLAB:

- The MATLAB prompt in the Student Version is

  `EDU>>`

- The window title bars include the words

  `<Student Version>`

- All printouts contain the footer

  `Student Version of MATLAB`

  This footer is not an option that can be turned off; it will always appear in your printouts.

- The Documentation CD must be in your CD-ROM drive to start MATLAB. Once MATLAB starts, you can remove the CD. However, to access the online documentation, the CD must be in the CD-ROM drive.

Simulink

This Student Version contains the complete Simulink product, which is used with MATLAB to model, simulate, and analyze dynamic systems.

Simulink Differences.

- Models are limited to 300 blocks.

Note You may encounter some demos that use more than 300 blocks. In these cases, a dialog will display stating that the block limit has been exceeded and the demo will not run.

- The window title bars include the words
  <Student Version>

- All printouts contain the footer
  ```
  Student Version of MATLAB
  ```

  This footer is not an option that can be turned off; it will always appear in your printouts.

Note The Using Simulink documentation, which is accessible from the Help browser, contains all of the relevant information in the Learning Simulink book plus additional advanced information.

Symbolic Math Toolbox

The Symbolic Math Toolbox included with this Student Version lets you access all of the functions in the professional version of the Symbolic Math Toolbox except `maple`, `mapleinit`, `mfun`, `mfunlist`, and `mhelp`. For a complete list of all the available functions, see Appendix B, "Symbolic Math Toolbox Quick Reference," in Learning MATLAB.

Other Products

SimMechanics. With this product, you can build models with up to 20 mechanical bodies. This limit will accommodate models with as many as 120 degrees of freedom (a computationally intense simulation).

Obtaining Additional MathWorks Products

Many college courses recommend MATLAB as their standard instructional software. In some cases, the courses may require particular toolboxes, blocksets, or other products. Many of these products are available for student use. You may purchase and download these additional products at special student prices from the MathWorks Store at www.mathworks.com/store.

Some of the products you can purchase include

- Communications Blockset
- Control System Toolbox
- Fuzzy Logic Toolbox
- Image Processing Toolbox
- Neural Network Toolbox
- Optimization Toolbox
- Signal Processing Toolbox
- Statistics Toolbox
- Fixed-Point Blockset
- Stateflow® (A demo version of Stateflow is included with your Student Version.)

For an up-to-date list of available toolboxes and blocksets, visit the MathWorks Store.

Note The toolboxes and blocksets that are available for the MATLAB Student Version have the same functionality as the full, professional versions. The only restrictions are those described in "Differences Between the Student Version and the Professional Version" on page 1-3. Also, the student versions of the toolboxes and blocksets will only work with the Student Version. Likewise, the professional versions of the toolboxes and blocksets will not work with the Student Version.

Getting Started with Simulink

What I Want	What I Should Do
I need to install Simulink.	See Chapter 2, "Installation," in the Learning MATLAB book.
I want to start Simulink.	On all operating systems, your MathWorks Documentation CD must be in your CD-ROM drive to start MATLAB.
	(Microsoft Windows) Double-click the MATLAB icon on your desktop to start MATLAB. Click the Simulink icon on the toolbar to start Simulink.
	(Macintosh OS X) Double-click the LaunchMATLAB icon on your desktop to start MATLAB. Click the Simulink icon on the toolbar to start Simulink.
	(Linux) Enter the matlab command to start MATLAB. Click the Simulink icon on the toolbar to start Simulink.
I'm new to Simulink and want to learn it quickly.	Start by reading Learning Simulink. You'll learn how to model, simulate, and analyze dynamic systems. Since Simulink is graphical and interactive, this book encourages you to use it quickly. You can access the rest of the Simulink documentation through the online Help facility (Help).
I want to look at some samples of what you can do with Simulink.	There are numerous demonstrations included with Simulink. You can see the demos by clicking **Demos** in the Help Navigator or selecting **Demos** from the **Help** menu. There are Simulink demos for simple models, complex models, and other related products. You also will find a large selection of demos at www.mathworks.com/demos.

Finding Reference Information

What I Want	What I Should Do
I want to know how to use a specific Simulink block.	Use the online Help facility (Help). The Simulink blocks are described under Simulink (**Simulink -> Block Libraries**).
I want to find a block for a specific purpose but I don't know its name.	There are several choices: • See Appendix A, "Block Libraries," in this book for a list of Simulink blocks. • From Help, peruse the "Block Libraries" section under Simulink. • Use Index or Search from Help.
I want to know what blocks are available in a general area.	Use Help to see the "Block Libraries" section under Simulink, or see Appendix A, "Block Libraries," in this book for a list of Simulink blocks.

Troubleshooting and Other Resources

What I Want	What I Should Do
I have a Simulink specific problem I want help with.	Visit the Technical Support section (www.mathworks.com/support) of the MathWorks Web site.
I want to report a bug or make a suggestion.	Use Help or send e-mail to bugs@mathworks.com or suggest@mathworks.com.

Documentation Library

Your MATLAB Student Version contains much more documentation than the two printed books, Learning MATLAB and Learning Simulink. On your Documentation CD is a personal reference library of every book and reference page that is available for the Student Version. Access this documentation library from Help.

Note For an up-to-date list of products that are available for the Student Version, visit the MathWorks Store (www.mathworks.com/store). At the store you can also purchase printed manuals for the MATLAB family of products.

Accessing the Online Documentation

Access the online documentation directly from your Documentation CD. (Refer to Chapter 2, "Installation," in the Learning MATLAB book for specific information on configuring and accessing the online Help from the CD.)

1 Place the CD in your CD-ROM drive.

2 Select **Full Product Family Help** from the **Help** menu.

Help appears in a separate window.

Tutorials and reference for MATLAB

Tutorials and reference for Symbolic Math Toolbox

Tutorials and reference for Simulink

Tutorials and reference for Stateflow

Note When you start MATLAB for the first time, the Help Navigator displays entries for additional products. To learn how to change the displayed product list, see the "Product Filter" section in Learning MATLAB.

MathWorks Web Site

Use your browser to visit the MathWorks Web site, www.mathworks.com. You'll find lots of information about MathWorks products and how they are used in education and industry, product demos, and MATLAB based books. From the Web site you will also be able to access our technical support resources, view a library of user and MathWorks supplied M-files, and get information about products and upcoming events.

MathWorks Education Web Site

This education-specific Web site, www.mathworks.com/education, contains many resources for various branches of engineering, mathematics, and science. Many of these include teaching examples, books, and other related products. You will also find a comprehensive list of links to Web sites where MATLAB is used for teaching and research at universities.

MATLAB Related Books

Hundreds of MATLAB related books are available from many different publishers. An up-to-date list is available at www.mathworks.com/support/books.

MathWorks Store

The MathWorks Store (www.mathworks.com/store) gives you an easy way to purchase add-on products and documentation.

MATLAB Central — File Exchange/Newsgroup Access

MATLAB Central (www.mathworks.com/matlabcentral) provides Web-based access to the MATLAB specific Usenet newsgroup (comp.soft-sys.matlab) as well as an extensive library of user-contributed files called the MATLAB File Exchange.

The newsgroup, comp.soft-sys.matlab, is a gathering of professionals and students who use MATLAB and have questions or comments about it and its associated products. This is a great resource for posing questions and answering those of others. MathWorks staff also participates actively in this newsgroup.

1-11

MathWorks Web-Based Technical Support

You can access MathWorks technical support from the Support link on our Web site. You can peruse information by product or search for particular information in Technical Notes, Solutions, documentation, and more. You will find numerous examples of graphics, mathematics, API, Simulink models, and other topics. You can answer many of your questions by spending a few minutes with this around-the-clock resource.

Technical Support

Telephone and e-mail access to our technical support staff is not available for students running the Student Version of MATLAB unless you are experiencing difficulty installing or downloading MATLAB or related products. There are numerous other vehicles of technical support that you can use. The "Additional Sources of Information" section in the CD holder identifies the ways to obtain support.

After checking the available MathWorks sources for help, if you still cannot resolve your problem, you should contact your instructor. Your instructor should be able to help you, but if not, there is telephone and e-mail technical support for registered instructors who have adopted the MATLAB Student Version in their courses.

Product Registration

Visit the MathWorks Web site (`www.mathworks.com/student`) and register your Student Version.

Registered users of the MATLAB Student Version can search our Solutions Database, get answers to Hot Topics, or use the Index of Examples located on the Technical Support Web site at `www.mathworks.com/support` to answer product questions.

About Simulink

Welcome to Simulink! In the last few years, Simulink has become the most widely used software package in academia and industry for modeling and simulating dynamic systems.

Simulink encourages you to try things out. You can easily build models from scratch, or take an existing model and add to it. Simulations are interactive, so you can change parameters while running a simulation and immediately see what happens. You have instant access to all of the analysis tools in MATLAB, so you can take the results and analyze and visualize them. We hope that you will get a sense of the *fun* of modeling and simulation, through an environment that encourages you to pose a question, model it, and see what happens.

With Simulink, you can move beyond idealized linear models to explore more realistic nonlinear models, factoring in friction, air resistance, gear slippage, hard stops, and the other things that describe real-world phenomena. It turns your computer into a lab for modeling and analyzing systems that simply wouldn't be possible or practical otherwise, whether analyzing the behavior of an automotive clutch system, the flutter of an airplane wing, the dynamics of a predator-prey model, or the effect of the monetary supply on the economy.

Simulink is also practical. With thousands of engineers around the world using it to model and solve real problems, knowledge of this tool will serve you well throughout your professional career.

We hope you enjoy exploring the software.

What Is Simulink?

Simulink is a software package for modeling, simulating, and analyzing dynamic systems. It supports linear and nonlinear systems, modeled in continuous time, sampled time, or a hybrid of the two. Systems can also be multirate, i.e., have different parts that are sampled or updated at different rates.

For modeling, Simulink provides a graphical user interface (GUI) for building models as block diagrams, using click-and-drag mouse operations. With this interface, you can draw the models just as you would with pencil and paper (or as most textbooks depict them). This is a far cry from previous simulation packages that require you to formulate differential equations and difference equations in a language or program. Simulink includes a comprehensive block library of sinks, sources, linear and nonlinear components, and connectors. You can also customize and create your own blocks. For information on creating your own blocks, see the separate Writing S-Functions guide under Simulink in Help.

Models are hierarchical, so you can build models using both top-down and bottom-up approaches. You can view the system at a high level, then double-click on blocks to go down through the levels to see increasing levels of model detail. This approach provides insight into how a model is organized and how its parts interact.

After you define a model, you can simulate it, using a choice of integration methods, either from the Simulink menus or by entering commands in the MATLAB Command Window. The menus are particularly convenient for interactive work, while the command-line approach is very useful for running a batch of simulations (for example, if you are doing Monte Carlo simulations or want to sweep a parameter across a range of values). Using scopes and other display blocks, you can see the simulation results while the simulation is running. In addition, you can change parameters and immediately see what happens, for "what if" exploration. The simulation results can be put in the MATLAB workspace for postprocessing and visualization.

Model analysis tools include linearization and trimming tools, which can be accessed from the MATLAB command line, plus the many tools in MATLAB and its application toolboxes. And because MATLAB and Simulink are integrated, you can simulate, analyze, and revise your models in either environment at any point.

What Is Stateflow?

Stateflow is an interactive design tool for modeling and simulating complex reactive systems. Tightly integrated with Simulink and MATLAB, Stateflow provides Simulink users with an elegant solution for designing embedded systems by giving them an efficient way to incorporate complex control and supervisory logic within their Simulink models.

With Stateflow, you can quickly develop graphical models of event-driven systems using finite state machine theory, statechart formalisms, and flow diagram notation. Together, Stateflow and Simulink serve as an executable specification and virtual prototype of your system design. For information on Stateflow, see the Stateflow and Stateflow Coder User's Guide, which is accessible from Help.

Note Your MATLAB Student Version includes a demo version of Stateflow.

2

Quick Start

The following sections use examples to give you a quick introduction to using Simulink to model and simulate dynamic systems.

Running a Demo Model

An interesting demo program provided with Simulink models the thermodynamics of a house. To run this demo, follow these steps:

1 Start MATLAB. See your MATLAB documentation if you're not sure how to do this.

2 Run the demo model by typing `thermo` in the MATLAB Command Window. This command starts up Simulink and creates a model window that contains this model.

3 Double-click the Scope block labeled Thermo Plots.

The Scope block displays two plots labeled Indoor vs. Outdoor Temp and Heat Cost ($), respectively.

4 To start the simulation, pull down the **Simulation** menu and choose the **Start** command (or, on Microsoft Windows, click the **Start** button on the Simulink toolbar). As the simulation runs, the indoor and outdoor

temperatures appear in the Indoor vs. Outdoor Temp plot and the cumulative heating cost appears in the Heat Cost ($) plot.

5 To stop the simulation, choose the **Stop** command from the **Simulation** menu (or click the **Pause** button on the toolbar). If you want to explore other parts of the model, look over the suggestions in "Some Things to Try" on page 2-4.

6 When you're finished running the simulation, close the model by choosing **Close** from the **File** menu.

Description of the Demo

The demo models the thermodynamics of a house using a simple model. The thermostat is set to 70 degrees Fahrenheit and is affected by the outside temperature, which varies by applying a sine wave with amplitude of 15 degrees to a base temperature of 50 degrees. This simulates daily temperature fluctuations.

The model uses subsystems to simplify the model diagram and create reusable systems. A subsystem is a group of blocks that is represented by a Subsystem block. This model contains five subsystems: one named Thermostat, one named House, and three Temp Convert subsystems (two convert Fahrenheit to Celsius, one converts Celsius to Fahrenheit).

The internal and external temperatures are fed into the House subsystem, which updates the internal temperature. Double-click the House block to see the underlying blocks in that subsystem.

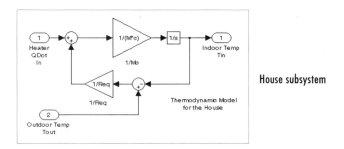

House subsystem

The Thermostat subsystem models the operation of a thermostat, determining when the heating system is turned on and off. Double-click the block to see the underlying blocks in that subsystem.

Thermostat subsystem

Both the outside and inside temperatures are converted from Fahrenheit to Celsius by identical subsystems.

Fahrenheit to Celsius conversion (F2C)

When the heat is on, the heating costs are computed and displayed on the Heat Cost (\$) plot on the Thermo Plots Scope. The internal temperature is displayed on the Indoor Temp Scope.

Some Things to Try

Here are several things to try to see how the model responds to different parameters:

- Each Scope block contains one or more signal display areas and controls that enable you to select the range of the signal displayed, zoom in on a portion of the signal, and perform other useful tasks. The horizontal axis represents time and the vertical axis represents the signal value.

- The Constant block labeled Set Point (at the top left of the model) sets the desired internal temperature. Open this block and reset the value to 80 degrees. See how the indoor temperature and heating costs change. Also, adjust the outside temperature (the Avg Outdoor Temp block) and see how it affects the simulation.

- Adjust the daily temperature variation by opening the Sine Wave block labeled Daily Temp Variation and changing the **Amplitude** parameter.

What This Demo Illustrates

This demo illustrates several tasks commonly used when you are building models:

- Running the simulation involves specifying parameters and starting the simulation with the **Start** command, described in "Diagnosing Simulation Errors" on page 8-35.

- You can encapsulate complex groups of related blocks in a single block, called a subsystem. See "Creating Subsystems" on page 5-19 for more information.

- You can create a customized icon and design a dialog box for a block by using the masking feature, described in detail in Chapter 10, "Creating Masked Subsystems." In the thermo model, all Subsystem blocks have customized icons created using the masking feature.

- Scope blocks display graphic output much as an actual oscilloscope does.

Other Useful Demos

Other demos illustrate useful modeling concepts. You can access these demos from the MATLAB Command Window:

1 Click the **Start** button on the bottom left corner of the MATLAB Command Window.

The **Start** menu appears.

2 Select **Demos** from the menu.

The MATLAB Help browser appears with the **Demos** pane selected.

3 Click the **Simulink** entry in the **Demos** pane.

The entry expands to show groups of Simulink demos. Use the browser to navigate to demos of interest. The browser displays explanations of each demo and includes a link to the demo itself. Click on a demo link to start the demo.

Building a Simple Model

This example shows you how to build a model using many of the model-building commands and actions you will use to build your own models. The instructions for building this model in this section are brief. All the tasks are described in more detail in the next chapter.

The model integrates a sine wave and displays the result along with the sine wave. The block diagram of the model looks like this.

To create the model, first enter `simulink` in the MATLAB Command Window. On Microsoft Windows, the Simulink Library Browser appears.

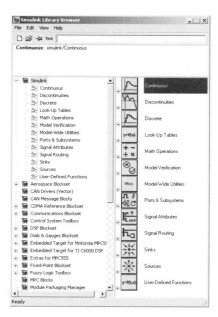

On the Macintosh or Linux, the Simulink library window appears.

To create a new model on the Macintosh or Linux, select **Model** from the **New** submenu of the Simulink library window's **File** menu. To create a new model on Windows, select the New Model button on the Library Browser's toolbar.

New model button ———

Simulink opens a new model window.

To create this model, you need to copy blocks into the model from the following Simulink block libraries:

- Sources library (the Sine Wave block)
- Sinks library (the Scope block)
- Continuous library (the Integrator block)
- Signal Routing library (the Mux block)

You can copy a Sine Wave block from the Sources library, using the Library Browser (Windows only) or the Sources library window (the Macintosh and Linux and Windows).

To copy the Sine Wave block from the Library Browser, first expand the Library Browser tree to display the blocks in the Sources library. Do this by clicking the Sources node to display the Sources library blocks. Finally, click the Sine Wave node to select the Sine Wave block.

Here is how the Library Browser should look after you have done this.

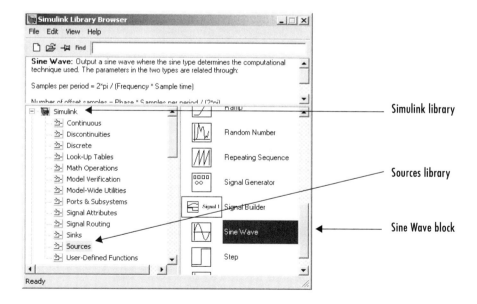

Simulink library

Sources library

Sine Wave block

Now drag the Sine Wave block from the browser and drop it in the model window. Simulink creates a copy of the Sine Wave block at the point where you dropped the node icon.

To copy the Sine Wave block from the Sources library window, open the Sources window by double-clicking the Sources icon in the Simulink library window. (On Windows, you can open the Simulink library window by right-clicking the Simulink node in the Library Browser and then clicking the resulting **Open Library** button.)

Simulink displays the Sources library window.

The Sine Wave block

Now drag the Sine Wave block from the Sources window to your model window.

Copy the rest of the blocks in a similar manner from their respective libraries into the model window. You can move a block from one place in the model window to another by dragging the block. You can move a block a short distance by selecting the block, then pressing the arrow keys.

With all the blocks copied into the model window, the model should look something like this.

If you examine the block icons, you see an angle bracket on the right of the Sine Wave block and two on the left of the Mux block. The > symbol pointing out of a block is an *output port*; if the symbol points to a block, it is an *input port*. A signal travels out of an output port and into an input port of another block through a connecting line. When the blocks are connected, the port symbols disappear.

Now it's time to connect the blocks. Connect the Sine Wave block to the top input port of the Mux block. Position the pointer over the output port on the right side of the Sine Wave block. Notice that the cursor shape changes to crosshairs.

Hold down the mouse button and move the cursor to the top input port of the Mux block.

Notice that the line is dashed while the mouse button is down and that the cursor shape changes to double-lined crosshairs as it approaches the Mux block.

Now release the mouse button. The blocks are connected. You can also connect the line to the block by releasing the mouse button while the pointer is inside the icon. If you do, the line is connected to the input port closest to the cursor's position.

If you look again at the model at the beginning of this section (see "Building a Simple Model" on page 2-7), you'll notice that most of the lines connect output ports of blocks to input ports of other blocks. However, one line connects a *line* to the input port of another block. This line, called a *branch line*, connects the Sine Wave output to the Integrator block, and carries the same signal that passes from the Sine Wave block to the Mux block.

Drawing a branch line is slightly different from drawing the line you just drew. To weld a connection to an existing line, follow these steps:

1 First, position the pointer *on the line* between the Sine Wave and the Mux block.

2 Press and hold down the **Ctrl** key (or click the right mouse button). Press the mouse button, then drag the pointer to the Integrator block's input port or over the Integrator block itself.

3 Release the mouse button. Simulink draws a line between the starting point and the Integrator block's input port.

Finish making block connections. When you're done, your model should look something like this.

Now, open the Scope block to view the simulation output. Keeping the Scope window open, set up Simulink to run the simulation for 10 seconds. First, set

the simulation parameters by choosing **Simulation Parameters** from the
Simulation menu.

On the dialog box that appears, notice that the **Stop time** is set to 10.0 (its
default value).

Stop time parameter

Close the **Simulation Parameters** dialog box by clicking the **OK** button.
Simulink applies the parameters and closes the dialog box.

Choose **Start** from the **Simulation** menu and watch the traces of the Scope
block's input.

The simulation stops when it reaches the stop time specified in the **Simulation Parameters** dialog box or when you choose **Stop** from the **Simulation** menu or click the **Stop** button on the model window's toolbar (Windows only).

To save this model, choose **Save** from the **File** menu and enter a filename and location. That file contains the description of the model.

To terminate Simulink and MATLAB, choose **Exit MATLAB** (on a Microsoft Windows system) or **Quit MATLAB** (on a Macintosh or Linux system). You can also enter quit in the MATLAB Command Window. If you want to leave Simulink but not terminate MATLAB, just close all Simulink windows.

This exercise shows you how to perform some commonly used model-building tasks. These and other tasks are described in more detail in Chapter 5, "Creating a Model."

Setting Simulink Preferences

The MATLAB **Preferences** dialog box allows you to specify default settings for many Simulink options. To display the **Preferences** dialog box, select **Preferences** from the Simulink **File** menu.

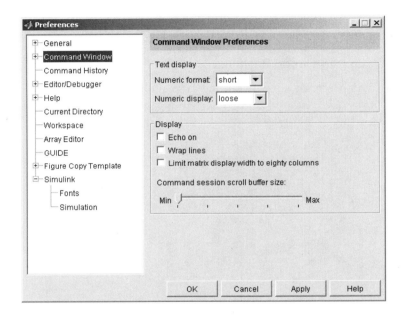

Miscellaneous Preferences

Selecting Simulink in the left hand pane of the preferences dialog box displays a **Simulink Preferences** pane on the right side of the dialog box.

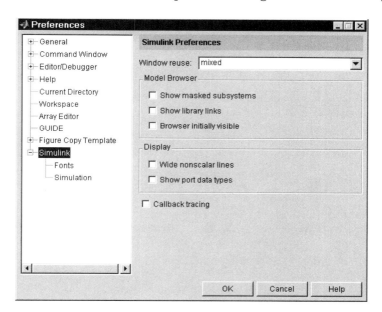

This pane allows you to specify the following Simulink preferences.

Window reuse

Specifies whether Simulink uses existing windows or opens new windows to display a model's subsystems (see "Window Reuse" on page 5-22).

Model Browser

Specifies whether Simulink displays the browser when you open a model and whether the browser shows blocks imported from subsystems and the contents of masked subsystems (see "The Model Browser" on page 9-8).

Display

Specifies whether to use thick lines to display nonscalar connections between blocks and whether to display port data types on the block diagram (see "Displaying Signals" on page 7-13).

Callback tracing

Specifies whether to display the model callbacks that Simulink invokes when simulating a model (see "Using Callback Routines" on page 5-48).

Font Preferences

Selecting the Fonts subnode of the Simulink node in the left hand side of the dialog box displays a stack of tabbed panes on the right side of the dialog box.

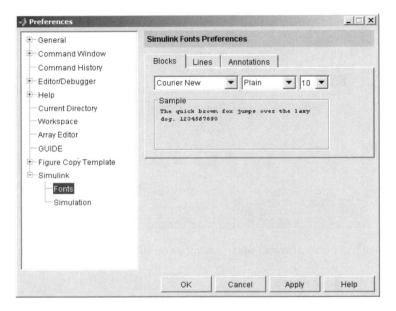

The panes allow you to specify your preferred fonts for block and line labels and model annotations, respectively.

Simulation Preferences

Selecting the Simulation node beneath the Simulink node in the left hand side of the dialog box displays a stack of tabbed panes on the right side of the dialog box.

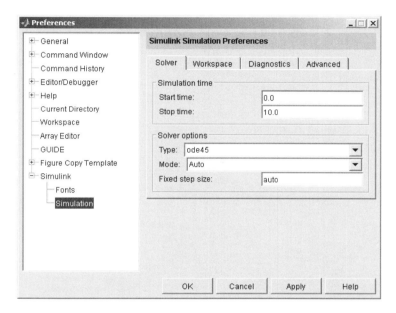

The panes allow you to specify the following preferences.

Solver

Specifies simulation solver options (see "The Solver Pane" on page 8-7).

Workspace

Specifies workspace options for simulating a model (see "The Workspace I/O Pane" on page 8-17).

Diagnostics

Specifies diagnostic options for simulating a model (see "The Diagnostics Pane" on page 8-24).

Advanced

Specifies advanced simulation preferences (see "The Advanced Pane" on page 8-28).

How Simulink Works

The following sections explain how Simulink models and simulates dynamic systems. This information can be helpful in creating models and interpreting simulation results.

What Is Simulink

Simulink is a software package that enables you to model, simulate, and analyze systems whose outputs change over time. Such systems are often referred to as dynamic systems. Simulink can be used to explore the behavior of a wide range of real-world dynamic systems, including electrical circuits, shock absorbers, braking systems, and many other electrical, mechanical, and thermodynamic systems.

Simulating a dynamic system is a two-step process with Simulink. First, you create a graphical model of the system to be simulated, using the Simulink model editor. The model depicts the time-dependent mathematical relationships among the system's inputs, states, and outputs (see "Modeling Dynamic Systems" on page 3-3). Then, you use Simulink to simulate the behavior of the system over a specified time span. Simulink uses information that you entered into the model to perform the simulation (see "Simulating Dynamic Systems" on page 3-8).

Modeling Dynamic Systems

Simulink provides a library browser that allows you to select blocks from libraries of standard blocks (see the "Block Reference" in the online Simulink Help) and a graphical editor that allows you to draw lines connecting the blocks (see Chapter 5, "Creating a Model"). You can model virtually any real-world dynamic system by selecting and interconnecting the appropriate Simulink blocks.

Block Diagrams

A Simulink block diagram is a pictorial model of a dynamic system. It consists of a set of symbols, called blocks, interconnected by lines. Each block represents an elementary dynamic system that produces an output either continuously (a continuous block) or at specific points in time (a discrete block). The lines represent connections of block inputs to block outputs. Every block in a block diagram is an instance of a specific type of block. The type of the block determines the relationship between a block's outputs and its inputs, states, and time. A block diagram can contain any number of instances of any type of block needed to model a system.

Note The MATLAB Based Books page on the MathWorks Web site includes texts that discuss the use of block diagrams in general, and Simulink in particular, to model dynamic systems.

Blocks

Blocks represent elementary dynamic systems that Simulink knows how to simulate. A block comprises one or more of the following: a set of inputs, a set of states, and a set of outputs.

A block's output is a function of time and the block's inputs and states (if any). The specific function that relates a block's output to its inputs, states, and time depends on the type of block of which the block is an instance.

States

For some types of blocks, some block outputs depend on variables called states. The states, in turn, depend on previous state values and current inputs. Blocks with states are said to have memory because such blocks must store the previous values of their states in order to compute the current values of the states.

The Simulink Integrator block is an example of a block that has a state. The Integrator block outputs the integral of the input signal from the start of the simulation to the current time. The integral at the current time step depends on the history of the Integrator block's input. The integral therefore is a state of the Integrator block and is, in fact, its only state. Another example of a block with states is the Simulink Memory block. A Memory block stores the values of its inputs at the current simulation time and outputs them at a later time. The states of a Memory block are the previous values of its inputs.

The Simulink Gain block is an example of a stateless block. A Gain block outputs its input signal multiplied by a constant called the gain. The output of a Gain block is determined entirely by the current value of the input and the gain, which does not vary. A Gain block therefore has no states. Other examples of stateless blocks include the Sum and Product blocks. The output of these blocks is purely a function of the current values of their inputs (the sum in one case, the product in the other). Thus, these blocks have no states.

System Functions

Each Simulink block type is associated with a set of system functions that specify the time-dependent relationships among its inputs, states, and outputs. The system functions include

- An output function, f_o, that relates the system's outputs to its inputs, states, and time

- An update function, f_u, that relates the future values of the system's discrete states to the current time, inputs, and states

- A derivative function, f_d, that relates the derivatives of the system's continuous states to time and the present values of the block's states and inputs

Symbolically, the system functions can be expressed as follows

$$y = f_o(t, x, u) \qquad \text{Output function}$$

$$x_{d_{k+1}} = f_u(t, x, u) \qquad \text{Update function}$$

$$x'_c = f_d(t, x, u) \qquad \text{Derivative function}$$

$$\text{where} \quad x = \begin{bmatrix} x_c \\ x_{d_k} \end{bmatrix}$$

where t is the current time, x is the block's states, u is the block's inputs, y is the block's outputs, x_d is the block's discrete derivatives, and x'_c is the derivatives of the block's continuous states. During a simulation, Simulink invokes the system functions to compute the values of the system's states and outputs.

Block Parameters

Key properties of many standard blocks are parameterized. For example, the gain of the Simulink Gain block is a parameter. Each parameterized block has a block dialog that lets you set the values of the parameters when editing or simulating the model. You can use MATLAB expressions to specify parameter values. Simulink evaluates the expressions before running a simulation. You can change the values of parameters during a simulation. This allows you to determine interactively the most suitable value for a parameter.

A parameterized block effectively represents a family of similar blocks. For example, when creating a model, you can set the gain parameter of each instance of the Gain block separately so that each instance behaves differently. Because it allows each standard block to represent a family of blocks, block parameterization greatly increases the modeling power of the standard Simulink libraries.

Tunable Parameters

Many block parameters are tunable. A *tunable parameter* is a parameter whose value can change while Simulink is executing a model. For example, the gain parameter of the Gain block is tunable. You can alter the block's gain while a simulation is running. If a parameter is not tunable and the simulation is running, Simulink disables the dialog box control that sets the parameter. Simulink allows you to specify that all parameters in your model are nontunable except for those that you specify. This can speed up execution of large models and enable generation of faster code from your model. See "Model parameter configuration" on page 8-28 for more information.

Continuous Versus Discrete Blocks

The standard Simulink block set includes continuous blocks and discrete blocks. Continuous blocks respond continuously to continuously changing input. Discrete blocks, by contrast, respond to changes in input only at integer multiples of a fixed interval called the block's sample time. Discrete blocks hold their output constant between successive sample time hits. Each discrete block includes a sample time parameter that allows you to specify its sample rate. Examples of continuous blocks include the Constant block and the blocks in the Continuous block library. Examples of discrete blocks include the Discrete Pulse Generator and the blocks in the Discrete block library.

Many Simulink blocks, for example, the Gain block, can be either continuous or discrete, depending on whether they are driven by continuous or discrete blocks. A block that can be either discrete or continuous is said to have an implicit sample rate. The implicit sample time is continuous if any of the block's inputs are continuous. The implicit sample time is equal to the shortest input sample time if all the input sample times are integer multiples of the shortest time. Otherwise, the input sample time is equal to the *fundamental sample time* of the inputs, where the fundamental sample time of a set of sample times is defined as the greatest integer divisor of the set of sample times.

Simulink can optionally color code a block diagram to indicate the sample times of the blocks it contains, e.g., black (continuous), magenta (constant), yellow (hybrid), red (fastest discrete), and so on. See "Mixed Continuous and Discrete Systems" on page 3-32 for more information.

Subsystems

Simulink allows you to model a complex system as a set of interconnected subsystems each of which is represented by a block diagram. You create a subsystem using the Subsystem block and the Simulink model editor. You can embed subsystems within subsystems to any depth to create hierarchical models. You can create conditionally executed subsystems that are executed only when a transition occurs on a triggering or enabling input (see "Conditionally Executed Subsystems" in the online Help for Simulink).

Custom Blocks

Simulink allows you to create libraries of custom blocks that you can then use in your models. You can create a custom block either graphically or programmatically. To create a custom block graphically, you draw a block diagram representing the block's behavior, wrap this diagram in an instance of the Simulink Subsystem block, and provide the block with a parameter dialog, using the Simulink block mask facility. To create a block programmatically, you create an M-file or a MEX-file that contains the block's system functions (see *Writing S-Functions* in the online Help for Simulink). The resulting file is called an S-function. You then associate the S-function with instances of the Simulink S-Function block in your model. You can add a parameter dialog to your S-Function block by wrapping it in a Subsystem block and adding the parameter dialog to the Subsystem block.

Signals

Simulink uses the term *signal* to refer to the output values of blocks. Simulink allows you to specify a wide range of signal attributes, including signal name, data type (e.g., 8-bit, 16-bit, or 32-bit integer), numeric type (real or complex), and dimensionality (one-dimensional or two-dimensional array). Many blocks can accept or output signals of any data or numeric type and dimensionality. Others impose restrictions on the attributes of the signals they can handle.

Solvers

A Simulink model specifies the time derivatives of its continuous states but not the values of the states themselves. Thus, when simulating a system, Simulink must compute continuous states by numerically integrating their state derivatives. There are a variety of general-purpose numerical integration techniques, each having advantages in specific applications. Simulink provides implementations, called ordinary differential equation (ODE) solvers, of the most stable, efficient, and accurate of these numerical integration methods. You can specify the solver to use in the model or when running a simulation.

Simulating Dynamic Systems

Simulating a dynamic system refers to the process of computing a system's states and outputs over a span of time, using information provided by the system's model. Simulink simulates a system when you choose **Start** from the model editor's **Simulation** menu, with the system's model open.

Simulation of the system occurs in two phases: model initialization and model execution.

Model Initialization Phase

During the initialization phase, Simulink

1 Evaluates the model's block parameter expressions to determine their values.

2 Determines signal attributes, e.g., name, data type, numeric type, and dimensionality, not explicitly specified by the model and checks that each block can accept the signals connected to its inputs.

Simulink uses a process called attribute propagation to determine unspecified attributes. This process entails propagating the attributes of a source signal to the inputs of the blocks that it drives.

3 Determined memory needed for work vectors, states, and run-time parameters for each block

4 Performs block reduction optimizations.

5 Flattens the model hierarchy by replacing virtual subsystems with the blocks that they contain (see "Atomic Versus Virtual Subsystems" on page 3-12).

6 Sorts the blocks into the order in which they need to be executed during the execution phase (see "Determining Block Update Order" on page 3-10).

7 Determines the sample times of all blocks in the model whose sample times you did not explicitly specify.

8 Allocates and initializes memory used to store the current values of each block's states and outputs.

Model Execution Phase

The simulation now enters the model execution phase. In this phase, Simulink successively computes the states and outputs of the system at intervals from the simulation start time to the finish time, using information provided by the model. The successive time points at which the states and outputs are computed are called time steps. The length of time between steps is called the step size. The step size depends on the type of solver (see "Solvers" on page 3-12) used to compute the system's continuous states, the system's fundamental sample time (see "Modeling and Simulating Discrete Systems" on page 3-24), and whether the system's continuous states have discontinuities (see "Zero-Crossing Detection" on page 3-14).

At the start of the simulation, the model specifies the initial states and outputs of the system to be simulated. At each step, Simulink computes new values for the system's inputs, states, and outputs and updates the model to reflect the computed values. At the end of the simulation, the model reflects the final values of the system's inputs, states, and outputs. Simulink provides data display and logging blocks. You can display and/or log intermediate results by including these blocks in your model.

Processing at Each Time Step

At each time step, Simulink

1 Updates the outputs of the models' blocks in sorted order (see "Determining Block Update Order" on page 3-10).

   Simulink computes a block's outputs by invoking the block's output function. Simulink passes the current time and the block's inputs and states to the output function as it might require these arguments to compute the block's output. Simulink updates the output of a discrete block only if the current step is an integer multiple of the block's sample time.

2 Updates the states of the model's blocks in sorted order.

   Simulink computes a block's discrete states by invoking its discrete state update function. Simulink computes a block's continuous states by numerically integrating the time derivatives of the continuous states. It computes the time derivatives of the states by invoking the block's continuous derivatives function.

3 Optionally checks for discontinuities in the continuous states of blocks.

Simulink uses a technique called zero-crossing detection to detect discontinuities in continuous states. See "Zero-Crossing Detection" on page 3-14 for more information.

4 Computes the time for the next time step.

Simulink repeats steps 1 through 4 until the simulation stop time is reached.

Determining Block Update Order

During a simulation, Simulink updates the states and outputs of a model's blocks once per time step. The order in which the blocks are updated is therefore critical to the validity of the results. In particular, if a block's outputs are a function of its inputs at the current time step, the block must be updated after the blocks that drive its inputs. Otherwise, the block's outputs will be invalid. The order in which blocks are stored in a model file is not necessarily the order in which they need to be updated during a simulation. Consequently, Simulink sorts the blocks into the correct order during the model initialization phase.

Direct-Feedthrough Ports

In order to create a valid update ordering, Simulink categorizes a block's input ports according to the relationship of outputs to inputs. An input port whose current value determines the current value of one of the block's outputs is called a *direct-feedthrough* port. Examples of blocks that have direct-feedthrough ports include the Gain, Product, and Sum blocks. Examples of blocks that have non-direct-feedthrough inputs include the Integrator block (its output is a function purely of its state), the Constant block (it does not have an input), and the Memory block (its output is dependent on its input in the previous time step).

Block Sorting Rules

Simulink uses the following basic update rules to sort the blocks:

- Each block must be updated before any of the blocks whose direct-feedthrough ports it drives.

  This rule ensures that the direct-feedthrough inputs to blocks will be valid when the blocks are updated.

- Blocks that do not have direct feedthrough inputs can be updated in any order as long as they are updated before any blocks whose direct-feedthrough inputs they drive.

  Putting all blocks that do not have direct-feedthrough ports at the head of the update list in any order satisfies this rule. It thus allows Simulink to ignore these blocks during the sorting process.

The result of applying these rules is an update list in which blocks without direct feedthrough ports appear at the head of the list in no particular order followed by blocks with direct-feedthrough ports in the order required to supply valid inputs to the blocks they drive.

During the sorting process, Simulink checks for and flags the occurrence of algebraic loops, that is, signal loops in which a direct-feedthrough output of a block is connected directly or indirectly to the corresponding direct-feedthrough input of the block. Such loops seemingly create a deadlock condition, because Simulink needs the value of the direct-feedthrough input to compute the output. However, an algebraic loop can represent a set of simultaneous algebraic equations (hence the name) where the block's input and output are the unknowns. Further, these equations can have valid solutions at each time step. Accordingly, Simulink assumes that loops involving direct-feedthrough ports do, in fact, represent a solvable set of algebraic equations and attempts to solve them each time the block is updated during a simulation. For more information, see "Algebraic Loops" on page 3-18.

Block Priorities

Simulink allows you to assign update priorities to blocks (see "Assigning Block Priorities" on page 6-16). Simulink updates higher priority blocks before lower priority blocks. Simulink honors the priorities only if they are consistent with its block sorting rules.

Atomic Versus Virtual Subsystems

Subsystems can be virtual or atomic. Simulink ignores virtual subsystem boundaries when determining block update order. By contrast, Simulink executes all blocks within an atomic subsystem before moving on to the next block. Conditionally executed subsystems are atomic. Unconditionally executed subsystems are virtual by default. You can, however, designate an unconditionally executed subsystem as atomic (see Subsystem). This is useful if you need to ensure that a subsystem is executed in its entirety before any other block is executed.

Solvers

Simulink simulates a dynamic system by computing its states at successive time steps over a specified time span, using information provided by the model. The process of computing the successive states of a system from its model is known as solving the model. No single method of solving a model suffices for all systems. Accordingly, Simulink provides a set of programs, known as *solvers*, that each embody a particular approach to solving a model. The **Simulation Parameters** dialog box allows you to choose the solver most suitable for your model (see "Solvers" on page 8-8).

Fixed-Step Solvers Versus Variable-Step Solvers

Simulink solvers fall into two basic categories: fixed-step and variable-step.

Fixed-step solvers solve the model at regular time intervals from the beginning to the end of the simulation. The size of the interval is known as the step size. You can specify the step size or let the solver choose the step size. Generally decreasing the step size increases the accuracy of the results while increasing the time required to simulate the system.

Variable-step solvers vary the step size during the simulation, reducing the step size to increase accuracy when a model's states are changing rapidly and increasing the step size to avoid taking unnecessary steps when the model's states are changing slowly. Computing the step size adds to the computational overhead at each step but can reduce the total number of steps, and hence simulation time, required to maintain a specified level of accuracy for models with rapidly changing or piecewise continuous states.

Continuous Versus Discrete Solvers

Simulink provides both continuous and discrete solvers.

Continuous solvers use numerical integration to compute a model's continuous states at the current time step from the states at previous time steps and the state derivatives. Continuous solvers rely on the model's blocks to compute the values of the model's discrete states at each time step.

Mathematicians have developed a wide variety of numerical integration techniques for solving the ordinary differential equations (ODEs) that represent the continuous states of dynamic systems. Simulink provides an extensive set of fixed-step and variable-step continuous solvers, each implementing a specific ODE solution method (see "Solvers" on page 8-8).

Discrete solvers exist primarily to solve purely discrete models. They compute the next simulation time step for a model and nothing else. They do not compute continuous states and they rely on the model's blocks to update the model's discrete states.

Note You can use a continuous solver, but not a discrete solver, to solve a model that contains both continuous and discrete states. This is because a discrete solver does not handle continuous states. If you select a discrete solver for a continuous model, Simulink disregards your selection and uses a continuous solver instead when solving the model.

Simulink provides two discrete solvers, a fixed-step discrete solver and a variable-step discrete solver. The fixed-step solver by default chooses a step size and hence simulation rate fast enough to track state changes in the fastest block in your model. The variable-step solver adjusts the simulation step size to keep pace with the actual rate of discrete state changes in your model. This can avoid unnecessary steps and hence shorten simulation time for multirate models (see "Determining Step Size for Discrete Systems" on page 3-28 for more information).

Minor Time Steps

Some continuous solvers subdivide the simulation time span into major and minor time steps, where a minor time step represents a subdivision of the major time step. The solver produces a result at each major time step. It uses results at the minor time steps to improve the accuracy of the result at the major time step.

Zero-Crossing Detection

When simulating a dynamic system, Simulink checks for discontinuities in the system's state variables at each time step, using a technique known as zero-crossing detection. If Simulink detects a discontinuity within the current time step, it determines the precise time at which the discontinuity occurs and takes additional time steps before and after the discontinuity. This section explains why zero-crossing detection is important and how it works.

Discontinuities in state variables often coincide with significant events in the evolution of a dynamic system. For example, the instant when a bouncing ball hits the floor coincides with a discontinuity in its position. Because discontinuities often indicate a significant change in a dynamic system, it is important to simulate points of discontinuity precisely. Otherwise, a simulation could lead to false conclusions about the behavior of the system under investigation. Consider, for example, a simulation of a bouncing ball. If the point at which the ball hits the floor occurs between simulation steps, the simulated ball appears to reverse position in midair. This might lead an investigator to false conclusions about the physics of the bouncing ball.

To avoid such misleading conclusions, it is important that simulation steps occur at points of discontinuity. A simulator that relies purely on solvers to determine simulation times cannot efficiently meet this requirement. Consider, for example, a fixed-step solver. A fixed-step solver computes the values of state variables at integral multiples of a fixed step size. However, there is no guarantee that a point of discontinuity will occur at an integral multiple of the step size. You could reduce the step size to increase the probability of hitting a discontinuity, but this would greatly increase the execution time.

A variable-step solver appears to offer a solution. A variable-step solver adjusts the step size dynamically, increasing the step size when a variable is changing slowly and decreasing the step size when the variable changes rapidly. Around a discontinuity, a variable changes extremely rapidly. Thus, in theory, a variable-step solver should be able to hit a discontinuity precisely. The problem is that to locate a discontinuity accurately, a variable-step solver must again take many small steps, greatly slowing down the simulation.

How Zero-Crossing Detection Works

Simulink uses a technique known as zero-crossing detection to address this problem. With this technique, a block can register a set of zero-crossing variables with Simulink, each of which is a function of a state variable that can have a discontinuity. The zero-crossing function passes through zero from a positive or negative value when the corresponding discontinuity occurs. At the end of each simulation step, Simulink asks each block that has registered zero-crossing variables to update the variables. Simulink then checks whether any variable has changed sign since the last step. Such a change indicates that a discontinuity occurred in the current time step.

If any zero crossings are detected, Simulink interpolates between the previous and current values of each variable that changed sign to estimate the times of the zero crossings (e.g., discontinuities). Simulink then steps up to and over each zero crossing in turn. In this way, Simulink avoids simulating exactly at the discontinuity, where the value of the state variable might be undefined.

Zero-crossing detection enables Simulink to simulate discontinuities accurately without resorting to excessively small step sizes. Many Simulink blocks support zero-crossing detection. The result is fast and accurate simulation of all systems, including systems with discontinuities.

Implementation Details

An example of a Simulink block that uses zero crossings is the Saturation block. Zero crossings detect these state events in the Saturation block:

- The input signal reaches the upper limit.
- The input signal leaves the upper limit.
- The input signal reaches the lower limit.
- The input signal leaves the lower limit.

Simulink blocks that define their own state events are considered to have *intrinsic zero crossings*. If you need explicit notification of a zero-crossing event, use the Hit Crossing block. See "Blocks with Zero Crossings" on page 3-17 for a list of blocks that incorporate zero crossings.

The detection of a state event depends on the construction of an internal zero-crossing signal. This signal is not accessible by the block diagram. For the Saturation block, the signal that is used to detect zero crossings for the upper limit is zcSignal = UpperLimit - u, where u is the input signal.

Zero-crossing signals have a direction attribute, which can have these values:

- *rising* – A zero crossing occurs when a signal rises to or through zero, or when a signal leaves zero and becomes positive.
- *falling* – A zero crossing occurs when a signal falls to or through zero, or when a signal leaves zero and becomes negative.
- *either* – A zero crossing occurs if either a rising or falling condition occurs.

For the Saturation block's upper limit, the direction of the zero crossing is *either*. This enables the entering and leaving saturation events to be detected using the same zero-crossing signal.

If the error tolerances are too large, it is possible for Simulink to fail to detect a zero crossing. For example, if a zero crossing occurs within a time step, but the values at the beginning and end of the step do not indicate a sign change, the solver steps over the crossing without detecting it.

This figure shows a signal that crosses zero. In the first instance, the integrator steps over the event. In the second, the solver detects the event.

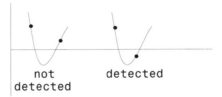

If you suspect this is happening, tighten the error tolerances to ensure that the solver takes small enough steps. For more information, see "Error Tolerances" on page 8-12.

Note Using the `Refine` output option (see "Refine output" on page 8-14) does not help locate the missed zero crossings. You should alter the maximum step size or output times.

Caveat

It is possible to create models that exhibit high-frequency fluctuations about a discontinuity (chattering). Such systems typically are not physically realizable; a massless spring, for example. Because chattering causes repeated detection of zero crossings, the step sizes of the simulation become very small, essentially halting the simulation.

If you suspect that this behavior applies to your model, you can disable zero-crossing detection by selecting the **Disable zero crossing detection** option on the **Advanced** pane of the **Simulation Parameters** dialog box (see "Zero-crossing detection" on page 8-31). Although disabling zero-crossing detection can alleviate the symptoms of this problem, you no longer benefit from the increased accuracy that zero-crossing detection provides. A better solution is to try to identify the source of the underlying problem in the model.

Blocks with Zero Crossings

The following table lists blocks that use zero crossings and explains how the blocks use the zero crossings:

Block	Description of Zero Crossing
Abs	One: to detect when the input signal crosses zero in either the rising or falling direction.
Backlash	Two: one to detect when the upper threshold is engaged, and one to detect when the lower threshold is engaged.
Dead Zone	Two: one to detect when the dead zone is entered (the input signal minus the lower limit), and one to detect when the dead zone is exited (the input signal minus the upper limit).
Hit Crossing	One: to detect when the input crosses the threshold.
Integrator	If the reset port is present, to detect when a reset occurs. If the output is limited, there are three zero crossings: one to detect when the upper saturation limit is reached, one to detect when the lower saturation limit is reached, and one to detect when saturation is left.
MinMax	One: for each element of the output vector, to detect when an input signal is the new minimum or maximum.

Block	Description of Zero Crossing (Continued)
Relay	One: if the relay is off, to detect the switch on point. If the relay is on, to detect the switch off point.
Relational Operator	One: to detect when the output changes.
Saturation	Two: one to detect when the upper limit is reached or left, and one to detect when the lower limit is reached or left.
Sign	One: to detect when the input crosses through zero.
Step	One: to detect the step time.
Subsystem	For conditionally executed subsystems: one for the enable port if present, and one for the trigger port, if present.
Switch	One: to detect when the switch condition occurs.

Algebraic Loops

Some Simulink blocks have input ports with *direct feedthrough*. This means that the output of these blocks cannot be computed without knowing the values of the signals entering the blocks at these input ports. Some examples of blocks with direct feedthrough inputs are as follows:

- The Math Function block
- The Gain block
- The Integrator block's initial condition ports
- The Product block
- The State-Space block when there is a nonzero D matrix
- The Sum block
- The Transfer Fcn block when the numerator and denominator are of the same order
- The Zero-Pole block when there are as many zeros as poles

An *algebraic loop* generally occurs when an input port with direct feedthrough is driven by the output of the same block, either directly, or by a feedback path through other blocks with direct feedthrough. (See "Nonalgebraic

Direct-Feedthrough Loops" on page 3-20 for an example of an exception to this general rule.) An example of an algebraic loop is this simple scalar loop.

Mathematically, this loop implies that the output of the Sum block is an algebraic state z constrained to equal the first input u minus z (i.e. $z = u - z$). The solution of this simple loop is $z = u/2$, but most algebraic loops cannot be solved by inspection. It is easy to create vector algebraic loops with multiple algebraic state variables $z1$, $z2$, etc., as shown in this model.

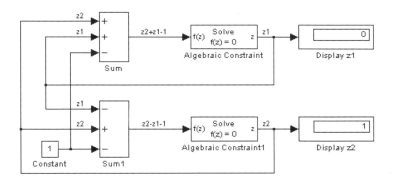

The Algebraic Constraint block is a convenient way to model algebraic equations and specify initial guesses. The Algebraic Constraint block constrains its input signal $F(z)$ to zero and outputs an algebraic state z. This block outputs the value necessary to produce a zero at the input. The output must affect the input through some feedback path. You can provide an initial guess of the algebraic state value in the block's dialog box to improve algebraic loop solver efficiency.

A scalar algebraic loop represents a scalar algebraic equation or constraint of the form $F(z) = 0$, where z is the output of one of the blocks in the loop and the function F consists of the feedback path through the other blocks in the loop to the input of the block. In the simple one-block example shown on the previous page, $F(z) = z - (u - z)$. In the vector loop example shown above, the equations are

$$z2 + z1 - 1 = 0$$
$$z2 - z1 - 1 = 0$$

Algebraic loops arise when a model includes an algebraic constraint $F(z) = 0$. This constraint might arise as a consequence of the physical interconnectivity of the system you are modeling, or it might arise because you are specifically trying to model a differential/algebraic system (DAE).

When a model contains an algebraic loop, Simulink calls a loop solving routine at each time step. The loop solver performs iterations to determine the solution to the problem (if it can). As a result, models with algebraic loops run slower than models without them.

To solve $F(z) = 0$, the Simulink loop solver uses Newton's method with weak line search and rank-one updates to a Jacobian matrix of partial derivatives. Although the method is robust, it is possible to create loops for which the loop solver will not converge without a good initial guess for the algebraic states z. You can specify an initial guess for a line in an algebraic loop by placing an IC block (which is normally used to specify an initial condition for a signal) on that line. As shown above, another way to specify an initial guess for a line in an algebraic loop is to use an Algebraic Constraint block.

Whenever possible, use an IC block or an Algebraic Constraint block to specify an initial guess for the algebraic state variables in a loop.

Nonalgebraic Direct-Feedthrough Loops

There are exceptions to the general rule that all loops comprising direct-feedthrough blocks are algebraic. The exceptions are

- Loops involving triggered subsystems
- A loop from the output to the reset port of an integrator

A triggered subsystem holds its outputs constant between trigger events (see "Triggered Subsystems" in the online Simulink Help). Thus, a solver can safely use the output from the system's previous time step to compute its input at the current time step. This is, in fact, what a solver does when it encounters a loop involving a triggered subsystem, thus eliminating the need for an algebraic loop solver.

Note Because a solver uses a triggered subsystem's previous output to compute feedback inputs, the subsystem, and any block in its feedback path, can exhibit a one-sample-time delay in its output. When simulating a system with triggered feedback loops, Simulink displays a warning to remind you that such delays can occur.

Consider, for example, the following system.

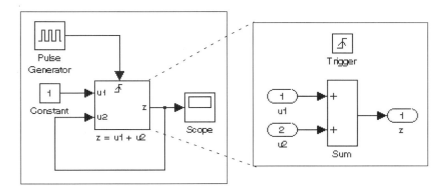

This system effectively solves the equation

```
z = 1 + u
```

where u is the value of z the last time the subsystem was triggered. The output of the system is a staircase function as illustrated by the display on the system's scope.

Now consider the effect of removing the trigger from the system shown in the previous example.

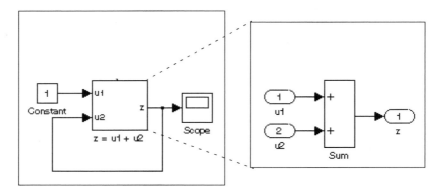

In this case, the input at the u2 port of the adder subsystem is equal to the subsystem's output at the current time step for every time step. The mathematical representation of this system

    z = z + 1

reveals that it has no mathematically valid solution.

Highlighting Algebraic Loops

You can cause Simulink to highlight algebraic loops when you update, simulate, or debug a model. Use the ashow command to highlight algebraic loops when debugging a model.

To cause Simulink to highlight algebraic loops that it detects when updating or simulating a model, set the Algebraic loop diagnostic on the **Diagnostics** pane of the **Simulation parameters** dialog box to Error (see "Configuration options" on page 8-25 for more information). This causes Simulink to display an error dialog (the Diagnostic Viewer) and recolor portions of the diagram that represent the algebraic loops that it detects. Simulink uses red to color the blocks and lines that constitute the loops. Closing the error dialog restores the diagram to its original colors.

For example, the following figure shows the block diagram of the `hydcyl` demo model in its original colors.

The following figure shows the diagram after updating when the `Algebraic loop diagnostic` is set to `Error`.

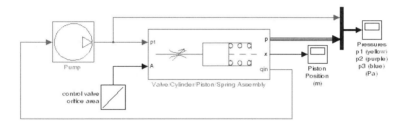

In this example, Simulink has colored the algebraic loop red, making it stand out from the rest of the diagram.

Modeling and Simulating Discrete Systems

Simulink has the ability to simulate discrete (sampled data) systems, including systems whose components operate at different rates (*multirate systems*) and systems that mix discrete and continuous components (*hybrid systems*). This capability stems from two key Simulink features:

- SampleTime block parameter

  Some Simulink blocks have a SampleTime parameter that you can use to specify the block's sample time, i.e., the rate at which it executes during simulation. Blocks that have this parameter include all the blocks in the Discrete library and some of the blocks in the Sources library, e.g., the Sine Wave and Pulse Generator blocks.

- Sample-time inheritance

  Most standard Simulink blocks can inherit their sample time from the blocks connected to their inputs. Exceptions include blocks in the Continuous library and blocks that do not have inputs (e.g., blocks from the Sources library). In some cases, source blocks can inherit the sample time of the block connected to its input.

The ability to specify sample times on a block-by-block basis, either directly through the SampleTime parameter or indirectly through inheritance, enables you to model systems containing discrete components operating at different rates and hybrid systems containing discrete and continuous components.

Specifying Sample Time

Simulink allows you to specify the sample time of any block that has a SampleTime parameter. You can use the block's parameter dialog box to set this parameter. You do this by entering the sample time in the **Sample time** field on the dialog box. You can enter either the sample time alone or a vector whose first element is the sample time and whose second element is an offset: $[T_s, T_o]$. Various values of the sample time and offset have special meanings.

The following table summarizes valid values for this parameter and how Simulink interprets them to determine a block's sample time.

Sample Time	Usage
$[T_s, T_o]$ $0 > T_s < T_{sim}$ $\lvert T_o \rvert < T_p$	Specifies that updates occur at simulation times $$t_n = n * T_s + \lvert T_o \rvert$$ where n is an integer in the range $1..T_{sim}/T_s$ and T_{sim} is the length of the simulation. Blocks that have a sample time greater than 0 are said to have a *discrete sample time*. The offset allows you to specify that Simulink update the block later in the sample interval than other blocks operating at the same rate.
$[0, 0], 0$	Specifies that updates occur at every major and minor time step. A block that has a sample time of 0 is said to have a *continuous sample time*.
$[0, 1]$	Specifies that updates occur only at major time steps, skipping minor time steps (see "Minor Time Steps" on page 3-13). This setting avoids unnecessary computations for blocks whose sample time cannot change between major time steps. The sample time of a block that executes only at major time steps is said to be *fixed in minor time step*.

Sample Time	Usage
[-1, 0], -1	If the block is not in a triggered subsystem, this setting specifies that the block inherits its sample time from the block connected to its input (inheritance) or, in some cases, from the block connected to its output (back inheritance). If the block is in a triggered subsystem, you must set the SampleTime parameter to this setting.
	Note that specifying sample-time inheritance for a source block can cause Simulink to assign an inappropriate sample time to the block if the source drives more than one block. For this reason, you should avoid specifying sample-time inheritance for source blocks. If you do, Simulink displays a warning message when you update or simulate the model.

Changing a Block's Sample Time

You cannot change the SampleTime parameter of a block while a simulation is running. If you want to change a block's sample time, you must stop and restart the simulation for the change to take effect.

Compiled Sample Time

During the compilation phase of a simulation, Simulink determines the sample time of the block from its SampleTime parameter (if it has a SampleTime parameter), sample-time inheritance, or block type (Continuous blocks always have a continuous sample time). It is this compiled sample time that determines the sample rate of a block during simulation. You can determine the compiled sample time of any block in a model by first updating the model and then getting the block's CompiledSampleTime parameter, using the get_param command.

Purely Discrete Systems

Purely discrete systems can be simulated using any of the solvers; there is no difference in the solutions. To generate output points only at the sample hits, choose one of the discrete solvers.

Multirate Systems

Multirate systems contain blocks that are sampled at different rates. These systems can be modeled with discrete blocks or with both discrete and continuous blocks. For example, consider this simple multirate discrete model.

For this example the DTF1 Discrete Transfer Fcn block's **Sample time** is set to [1 0.1], which gives it an offset of 0.1. The DTF2 Discrete Transfer Fcn block's **Sample time** is set to 0.7, with no offset.

Starting the simulation and plotting the outputs using the stairs function

```
[t,x,y] = sim('multirate', 3);
stairs(t,y)
```

produces this plot

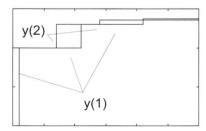

For the DTF1 block, which has an offset of 0.1, there is no output until t = 0.1. Because the initial conditions of the transfer functions are zero, the output of DTF1, y(1), is zero before this time.

Determining Step Size for Discrete Systems

Simulating a discrete system requires that the simulator take a simulation step at every *sample time hit*, that is, at integer multiples of the system's shortest sample time. Otherwise, the simulator might miss key transitions in the system's states. Simulink avoids this by choosing a simulation step size to ensure that steps coincide with sample time hits. The step size that Simulink chooses depends on the system's fundamental sample time and the type of solver used to simulate the system.

The *fundamental sample time* of a discrete system is the greatest integer divisor of the system's actual sample times. For example, suppose that a system has sample times of 0.25 and 0.5 second. The fundamental sample time in this case is 0.25 second. Suppose, instead, the sample times are 0.5 and 0.75 second. In this case, the fundamental sample time is again 0.25 second.

You can direct Simulink to use either a fixed-step or a variable-step discrete solver to solve a discrete system. A fixed-step solver sets the simulation step size equal to the discrete system's fundamental sample time. A variable-step solver varies the step size to equal the distance between actual sample time hits. The following diagram illustrates the difference between a fixed-step and a variable-size solver.

Fixed-Step Solver

Variable-Step Solver

In the diagram, arrows indicate simulation steps and circles represent sample time hits. As the diagram illustrates, a variable-step solver requires fewer simulation steps to simulate a system, if the fundamental sample time is less than any of the actual sample times of the system being simulated. On the other hand, a fixed-step solver requires less memory to implement and is faster if one of the system's sample times is fundamental. This can be an advantage in applications that entail generating code from a Simulink model (using Real-Time Workshop®).

Sample Time Propagation

The figure below illustrates a Discrete Filter block with a sample time of Ts driving a Gain block.

Because the Gain block's output is simply the input multiplied by a constant, its output changes at the same rate as the filter. In other words, the Gain block has an effective sample rate equal to that of the filter's sample rate. This is the fundamental mechanism behind sample time propagation in Simulink.

Simulink sets sample times for individual blocks according to these rules:

- Continuous blocks (e.g., Integrator, Derivative, Transfer Fcn, etc.) are, by definition, continuous.
- The Constant block is, by definition, constant.
- Discrete blocks (e.g., Zero-Order Hold, Unit Delay, Discrete Transfer Fcn, etc.) have sample times that are explicitly specified by the user on the block dialog boxes (see "Specifying Sample Time" on page 3-24).
- All other blocks have implicitly defined sample times that are based on the sample times of their inputs. For instance, a Gain block that follows an Integrator is treated as a continuous block, whereas a Gain block that follows a Zero-Order Hold is treated as a discrete block having the same sample time as the Zero-Order Hold block.

  For blocks whose inputs have different sample times, if all sample times are integer multiples of the fastest sample time, the block is assigned the sample time of the fastest input. If a variable-step solver is being used, the block is assigned the continuous sample time. If a fixed-step solver is being used and the greatest common divisor of the sample times (the fundamental sample time) can be computed, it is used. Otherwise continuous is used.

Under some circumstances, Simulink also back propagates sample times to source blocks if it can do so without affecting the output of a simulation. For instance, in the model below, Simulink recognizes that the Signal Generator block is driving a Discrete-Time Integrator block, so it assigns the Signal Generator block and the Gain block the same sample time as the Discrete-Time Integrator block.

You can verify this by selecting **Sample Time Colors** from the Simulink **Format** menu and noting that all blocks are colored red. Because the Discrete-Time Integrator block only looks at its input at its sample times, this change does not affect the outcome of the simulation but does result in a performance improvement.

Replacing the Discrete-Time Integrator block with a continuous Integrator block, as shown below, and recoloring the model by choosing **Update diagram** from the **Edit** menu cause the Signal Generator and Gain blocks to change to continuous blocks, as indicated by their being colored black.

Invariant Constants

Blocks either have explicitly defined sample times or inherit their sample times from blocks that feed them or are fed by them.

Simulink assigns Constant blocks a sample time of infinity, also referred to as a *constant sample time*. Other blocks have constant sample time if they receive their input from a Constant block and do not inherit the sample time of another block. This means that the output of these blocks does not change during the simulation unless the parameters are explicitly modified by the model user.

For example, in this model, both the Constant and Gain blocks have constant sample time.

Because Simulink supports the ability to change block parameters during a simulation, all blocks, even blocks having constant sample time, must generate their output at the model's effective sample time.

Note You can determine which blocks have constant sample time by selecting **Sample Time Colors** from the **Format** menu. Blocks having constant sample time are colored magenta.

Because of this feature, *all* blocks compute their output at each sample time hit, or, in the case of purely continuous systems, at every simulation step. For blocks having constant sample time whose parameters do not change during a simulation, evaluating these blocks during the simulation is inefficient and slows down the simulation.

You can set the inline parameters option (see "Inline parameters" on page 8-28) to remove all blocks having constant sample times from the simulation "loop." The effect of this feature is twofold. First, parameters for these blocks cannot be changed during a simulation. Second, simulation speed is improved. The speed improvement depends on model complexity, the number of blocks with constant sample time, and the effective sampling rate of the simulation.

Mixed Continuous and Discrete Systems

Mixed continuous and discrete systems are composed of both sampled and continuous blocks. Such systems can be simulated using any of the integration methods, although certain methods are more efficient and accurate than others. For most mixed continuous and discrete systems, the Runge-Kutta variable-step methods, ode23 and ode45, are superior to the other methods in terms of efficiency and accuracy. Because of discontinuities associated with the sample and hold of the discrete blocks, the ode15s and ode113 methods are not recommended for mixed continuous and discrete systems.

Simulink Basics

The following sections explain how to perform basic Simulink tasks.

Starting Simulink

To start Simulink, you must first start MATLAB. Consult your MATLAB documentation for more information. You can then start Simulink in two ways:

- Click the Simulink icon 📊 on the MATLAB toolbar.
- Enter the `simulink` command at the MATLAB prompt.

On Microsoft Windows platforms, starting Simulink displays the Simulink Library Browser.

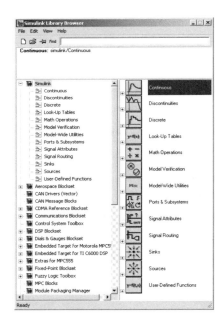

The Library Browser displays a tree-structured view of the Simulink block libraries installed on your system. You can build models by copying blocks from the Library Browser into a model window (this procedure is described later in this chapter).

On Macintosh or Linux platforms, starting Simulink displays the Simulink block library window.

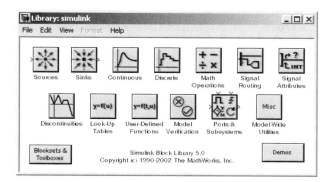

The Simulink library window displays icons representing the block libraries that come with Simulink. You can create models by copying blocks from the library into a model window.

Note On Windows, you can display the Simulink library window by right-clicking the Simulink node in the Library Browser window.

Opening Models

To edit an existing model diagram, either

- Click the **Open** button on the Library Browser's toolbar (Windows only) or select **Open** from the Simulink library window's **File** menu and then choose or enter the file name for the model to edit.

- Enter the name of the model (without the `.mdl` extension) in the MATLAB Command Window. The model must be in the current directory or on the path.

Entering Simulink Commands

You run Simulink and work with your model by entering commands. You can enter commands by

- Selecting items from the Simulink menu bar
- Selecting items from a context-sensitive Simulink menu (Windows only)
- Clicking buttons on the Simulink toolbar (Windows only)
- Entering commands in the MATLAB Command Window

Using the Simulink Menu Bar to Enter Commands

The Simulink menu bar appears near the top of each model window. The menu commands apply to the contents of that window.

Using Context-Sensitive Menus to Enter Commands

Simulink displays a context-sensitive menu when you click the right mouse button over a model or block library window. The contents of the menu depend on whether a block is selected. If a block is selected, the menu displays commands that apply only to the selected block. If no block is selected, the menu displays commands that apply to a model or library as a whole.

Using the Simulink Toolbar to Enter Commands

Model windows in the Windows version of Simulink optionally display a toolbar beneath the Simulink menu bar. To display the toolbar, select the **Toolbar** option on the Simulink **View** menu.

The toolbar contains buttons corresponding to frequently used Simulink commands, such as those for opening, running, and closing models. You can run such commands by clicking the corresponding button. For example, to open a Simulink model, click the button containing the open folder icon. You can determine which command a button executes by moving the mouse pointer over the button. A small window appears containing text that describes the button. The window is called a tooltip. Each button on the toolbar displays a tooltip when the mouse pointer hovers over it. You can hide the toolbar by clearing the **Toolbar** option on the Simulink **View** menu.

Using the MATLAB Window to Enter Commands

When you run a simulation and analyze its results, you can enter MATLAB commands in the MATLAB Command Window. See Chapter 8, "Running a Simulation," and Chapter 9, "Analyzing Simulation Results," for more information.

Undoing a Command

You can cancel the effects of up to 101 consecutive operations by choosing **Undo** from the **Edit** menu. You can undo these operations:

- Adding, deleting, or moving a block
- Adding, deleting, or moving a line
- Adding, deleting, or moving a model annotation
- Editing a block name
- Creating a subsystem (see "Undoing Subsystem Creation" on page 5-21 for more information)

You can reverse the effects of an **Undo** command by choosing **Redo** from the **Edit** menu.

Simulink Windows

Simulink uses separate windows to display a block library browser, a block library, a model, and graphical (scope) simulation output. These windows are not MATLAB figure windows and cannot be manipulated using Handle Graphics® commands.

Simulink windows are sized to accommodate the most common screen resolutions available. If you have a monitor with exceptionally high or low resolution, you might find the window sizes too small or too large. If this is the case, resize the window and save the model to preserve the new window dimensions.

Status Bar

The Windows version of Simulink displays a status bar at the bottom of each model and library window.

When a simulation is running, the status bar displays the status of the simulation, including the current simulation time and the name of the current solver. You can display or hide the status bar by selecting or clearing the **Status Bar** option on the Simulink **View** menu.

Zooming Block Diagrams

Simulink allows you to enlarge or shrink the view of the block diagram in the current Simulink window. To zoom a view:

- Select **Zoom In** from the **View** menu (or type r) to enlarge the view.
- Select **Zoom Out** from the **View** menu (or type v) to shrink the view.

- Select **Fit System to View** from the **View** menu (or press the space bar) to fit the diagram to the view.
- Select **Normal** from the **View** menu to view the diagram at actual size.

By default, Simulink fits a block diagram to view when you open the diagram either in the model browser's content pane or in a separate window. If you change a diagram's zoom setting, Simulink saves the setting when you close the diagram and restores the setting the next time you open the diagram. If you want to restore the default behavior, choose **Fit System to View** from the **View** menu the next time you open the diagram.

Saving a Model

You can save a model by choosing either the **Save** or **Save As** command from the **File** menu. Simulink saves the model by generating a specially formatted file called the *model file* (with the .mdl extension) that contains the block diagram and block properties.

If you are saving a model for the first time, use the **Save** command to provide a name and location for the model file. Model file names must start with a letter and can contain no more than 63 letters, numbers, and underscores. The file name must not be the same as that of a MATLAB command.

If you are saving a model whose model file was previously saved, use the **Save** command to replace the file's contents or the **Save As** command to save the model with a new name or location. You can also use the **Save As** command to save the model in a format compatible with previous releases of Simulink (see "Saving a Model in Earlier Formats" on page 4-9).

Simulink follows this procedure while saving a model:

1 If the mdl file for the model already exists, it is renamed as a temporary file.

2 Simulink executes all block PreSaveFcn callback routines, then executes the block diagram's PreSaveFcn callback routine.

3 Simulink writes the model file to a new file using the same name and an extension of mdl.

4 Simulink executes all block PostSaveFcn callback routines, then executes the block diagram's PostSaveFcn callback routine.

5 Simulink deletes the temporary file.

If an error occurs during this process, Simulink renames the temporary file to the name of the original model file, writes the current version of the model to a file with an .err extension, and issues an error message. Simulink performs steps 2 through 4 even if an error occurs in an earlier step.

Saving a Model in Earlier Formats

The **Save As** command allows you to save a model created with the latest version of Simulink in formats used by earlier versions of Simulink, including

Simulink 3 (Release 11), Simulink 4 (Release 12), and Simulink 4.1 (Release 12.1). You might want to do this, for example, if you need to make a model available to colleagues who have access only to one of these earlier versions of Simulink.

To save a model in earlier format:

1 Select **Save As** from the Simulink **File** menu.

   Simulink displays the **Save As** dialog box.

2 Select a format from the **Save as type** list on the dialog box.

3 Click the **Save** button.

When saving a model in an earlier version's format, Simulink saves the model in that format regardless of whether the model contains blocks and features that were introduced after that version. If the model does contain blocks or use features that postdate the earlier version, the model might not give correct results when run by the earlier version. For example, matrix and frame signals do not work in Release 11, because Release 11 does not have matrix and frame support. Similarly, models that contain unconditionally executed subsystems marked "Treat as atomic unit" might produce different results in Release 11, because Release 11 does not support unconditionally executed atomic subsystems.

The command converts blocks that postdate the earlier version into empty masked subsystem blocks colored yellow. For example, post-Release 11 blocks include

- Look-Up Table (n-D)
- Assertion
- Rate Transition
- PreLook-Up Index Search
- Interpolation (n-D)
- Direct Look-Up Table (n-D)
- Polynomial
- Matrix Concatenation
- Signal Specification
- Bus Creator
- If, WhileIterator, ForIterator, Assignment
- SwitchCase
- Bitwise Logical Operator

Post-Release 11 blocks from Simulink blocksets appear as unlinked blocks.

Printing a Block Diagram

You can print a block diagram by selecting **Print** from the **File** menu (on a Microsoft Windows system) or by using the print command in the MATLAB Command Window (on all platforms).

On a Microsoft Windows system, the **Print** menu item prints the block diagram in the current window.

Print Dialog Box

When you select the **Print** menu item, the **Print** dialog box appears. The **Print** dialog box enables you to selectively print systems within your model. Using the dialog box, you can print

- The current system only
- The current system and all systems above it in the model hierarchy
- The current system and all systems below it in the model hierarchy, with the option of looking into the contents of masked and library blocks
- All systems in the model, with the option of looking into the contents of masked and library blocks
- An overlay frame on each diagram

The portion of the **Print** dialog box that supports selective printing is similar on supported platforms. This figure shows how it looks on a Microsoft Windows system. In this figure, only the current system is to be printed.

When you select either the **Current system and below** or **All systems** option, two check boxes become enabled. In this figure, **All systems** is selected.

Selecting the **Look Under Mask Dialog** check box prints the contents of masked subsystems when encountered at or below the level of the current block. When you are printing all systems, the top-level system is considered the current block, so Simulink looks under any masked blocks encountered.

Selecting the **Expand Unique Library Links** check box prints the contents of library blocks when those blocks are systems. Only one copy is printed regardless of how many copies of the block are contained in the model. For more information about libraries, see "Working with Block Libraries" on page 6-25.

The print log lists the blocks and systems printed. To print the print log, select the **Include Print Log** check box.

Selecting the **Frame** check box prints a title block frame on each diagram. Enter the path to the title block frame in the adjacent edit box. You can create a customized title block frame, using the MATLAB frame editor. See `frameedit` in the online MATLAB reference for information on using the frame editor to create title block frames.

Print Command

The format of the `print` command is

```
print -ssys -device filename
```

sys is the name of the system to be printed. The system name must be preceded by the s switch identifier and is the only required argument. sys must be open or must have been open during the current session. If the system name contains spaces or takes more than one line, you need to specify the name as a string. See the examples below.

device specifies a device type. For a list and description of device types, see the documentation for the MATLAB print function.

filename is the PostScript file to which the output is saved. If filename exists, it is replaced. If filename does not include an extension, an appropriate one is appended.

For example, this command prints a system named untitled.

```
print -suntitled
```

This command prints the contents of a subsystem named Sub1 in the current system.

```
print -sSub1
```

This command prints the contents of a subsystem named Requisite Friction.

```
print (['-sRequisite Friction'])
```

The next example prints a system named Friction Model, a subsystem whose name appears on two lines. The first command assigns the newline character to a variable; the second prints the system.

```
cr = sprintf('\n');
print (['-sFriction' cr 'Model'])
```

To print the currently selected subsystem, enter

```
print(['-s', gcb])
```

Specifying Paper Size and Orientation

Simulink lets you specify the type and orientation of the paper used to print a model diagram. You can do this on all platforms by setting the model's PaperType and PaperOrientation properties, respectively (see "Model and Block Parameters" in the online documentation), using the set_param command. You can set the paper orientation alone, using the MATLAB orient command. On Windows, the **Print** and **Printer Setup** dialog boxes let you set the page type and orientation properties as well.

Positioning and Sizing a Diagram

You can use a model's PaperPositionMode and PaperPosition parameters to position and size the model's diagram on the printed page. The value of the PaperPosition parameter is a vector of form [left bottom width height]. The first two elements specify the bottom left corner of a rectangular area on the page, measured from the page's bottom left corner. The last two elements specify the width and height of the rectangle. When the model's PaperPositionMode is manual, Simulink positions (and scales, if necessary) the model's diagram to fit inside the specified print rectangle. For example, the following commands

```
vdp
set_param('vdp', 'PaperType', 'usletter')
set_param('vdp', 'PaperOrientation', 'landscape')
set_param('vdp', 'PaperPositionMode', 'manual')
set_param('vdp', 'PaperPosition', [0.5 0.5 4 4])
print -svdp
```

print the block diagram of the vdp sample model in the lower left corner of a U.S. letter-size page in landscape orientation.

If PaperPositionMode is auto, Simulink centers the model diagram on the printed page, scaling the diagram, if necessary, to fit the page.

Generating a Model Report

A Simulink model report is an HTML document that describes a model's structure and content. The report includes block diagrams of the model and its subsystems and the settings of its block parameters.

To generate a report for the current model:

1 Select **Print details** from the model's **File** menu.

The **Print Details** dialog box appears.

The dialog box allows you to select various report options (see "Model Report Options" on page 4-17).

2 Select the desired report options on the dialog box.

3 Select **Print**.

Simulink generates the HTML report and displays the in your system's default HTML browser.

While generating the report, Simulink displays status messages on a messages pane that replaces the options pane on the **Print Details** dialog box.

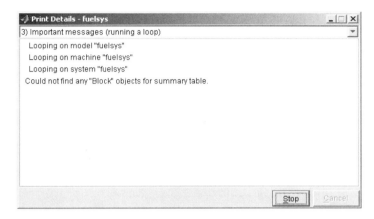

You can select the detail level of the messages from the list at the top of the messages pane. When the report generation process begins, the **Print** button on the **Print Details** dialog box changes to a **Stop** button. Clicking this button terminates the report generation. When the report generation process finishes, the **Stop** button changes to an **Options** button. Clicking this button redisplays the report generation options, allowing you to generate another report without having to reopen the **Print Details** dialog box.

Model Report Options

The **Print Details** dialog box allows you to select the following report options.

Directory

The directory where Simulink stores the HTML report that it generates. The options include your system's temporary directory (the default), your system's current directory, or another directory whose path you specify in the adjacent edit field.

Increment filename to prevent overwriting old files

Creates a unique report file name each time you generate a report for the same model in the current session. This preserves each report.

Current object

Include only the currently selected object in the report.

Current and above

Include the current object and all levels of the model above the current object in the report.

Current and below

Include the current object and all levels below the current object in the report.

Entire model

Include the entire model in the report.

Look under mask dialog

Include the contents of masked subsystems in the report.

Expand unique library links

Include the contents of library blocks that are subsystems. The report includes a library subsystem only once even if it occurs in more than one place in the model.

Summary of Mouse and Keyboard Actions

These tables summarize the use of the mouse and keyboard to manipulate blocks, lines, and signal labels. LMB means press the left mouse button; CMB, the center mouse button; and RMB, the right mouse button.

Manipulating Blocks

The following table lists mouse and keyboard actions that apply to blocks.

Task	Microsoft Windows	Macintosh or Linux
Select one block	LMB	LMB
Select multiple blocks	**Shift** + LMB	**Shift** + LMB; or CMB alone
Copy block from another window	Drag block	Drag block
Move block	Drag block	Drag block
Duplicate block	**Ctrl** + LMB and drag; or RMB and drag	**Ctrl** + LMB and drag; or RMB and drag
Connect blocks	LMB	LMB
Disconnect block	**Shift** + drag block	**Shift** + drag block; or CMB and drag
Open selected subsystem	**Enter**	**Return**
Go to parent of selected subsystem	**Esc**	**Esc**

4-19

Manipulating Lines

The following table lists mouse and keyboard actions that apply to lines.

Task	Microsoft Windows	Macintosh or Linux
Select one line	LMB	LMB
Select multiple lines	**Shift** + LMB	**Shift** + LMB; or CMB alone
Draw branch line	**Ctrl** + drag line; or RMB and drag line	**Ctrl** + drag line; or RMB + drag line
Route lines around blocks	**Shift** + draw line segments	**Shift** + draw line segments; or CMB and draw segments
Move line segment	Drag segment	Drag segment
Move vertex	Drag vertex	Drag vertex
Create line segments	**Shift** + drag line	**Shift** + drag line; or CMB + drag line

Manipulating Signal Labels

The next table lists mouse and keyboard actions that apply to signal labels.

Action	Microsoft Windows	Macintosh or Linux
Create signal label	Double-click line, then enter label	Double-click line, then enter label
Copy signal label	**Ctrl** + drag label	**Ctrl** + drag label
Move signal label	Drag label	Drag label
Edit signal label	Click in label, then edit	Click in label, then edit
Delete signal label	**Shift** + click label, then press **Delete**	**Shift** + click label, then press **Delete**

Manipulating Annotations

The next table lists mouse and keyboard actions that apply to annotations.

Action	Microsoft Windows	Macintosh or Linux
Create annotation	Double-click in diagram, then enter text	Double-click in diagram, then enter text
Copy annotation	**Ctrl** + drag label	**Ctrl** + drag label
Move annotation	Drag label	Drag label
Edit annotation	Click in text, then edit	Click in text, then edit
Delete annotation	**Shift** + select annotation, then press **Delete**	**Shift** + select annotation, then press **Delete**

Ending a Simulink Session

Terminate a Simulink session by closing all Simulink windows.

Terminate a MATLAB session by choosing one of these commands from the **File** menu:

- On a Microsoft Windows system: **Exit MATLAB**
- On a Macintosh or Linux system: **Quit MATLAB**

Creating a Model

The following sections explain how to create Simulink models of dynamic systems.

Creating a New Model

To create a new model, click the **New** button on the Library Browser's toolbar (Windows only) or choose **New** from the library window's **File** menu and select **Model**. You can move the window as you do other windows. Chapter 2, "Quick Start" describes how to build a simple model. "Modeling Equations" on page 8-2 describes how to build systems that model equations.

Selecting Objects

Many model building actions, such as copying a block or deleting a line, require that you first select one or more blocks and lines (objects).

Selecting One Object

To select an object, click it. Small black square "handles" appear at the corners of a selected block and near the end points of a selected line. For example, the figure below shows a selected Sine Wave block and a selected line.

When you select an object by clicking it, any other selected objects are deselected.

Selecting More Than One Object

You can select more than one object either by selecting objects one at a time, by selecting objects located near each other using a bounding box, or by selecting the entire model.

Selecting Multiple Objects One at a Time

To select more than one object by selecting each object individually, hold down the **Shift** key and click each object to be selected. To deselect a selected object, click the object again while holding down the **Shift** key.

Selecting Multiple Objects Using a Bounding Box

An easy way to select more than one object in the same area of the window is to draw a bounding box around the objects:

1 Define the starting corner of a bounding box by positioning the pointer at one corner of the box, then pressing and holding down the mouse button. Notice the shape of the cursor.

2 Drag the pointer to the opposite corner of the box. A dotted rectangle encloses the selected blocks and lines.

3 Release the mouse button. All blocks and lines at least partially enclosed by the bounding box are selected.

Selecting the Entire Model

To select all objects in the active window, choose **Select All** from the **Edit** menu. You cannot create a subsystem by selecting blocks and lines in this way. For more information, see "Creating Subsystems" on page 5-19.

Specifying Block Diagram Colors

Simulink allows you to specify the foreground and background colors of any block or annotation in a diagram, as well as the diagram's background color. To set the background color of a block diagram, select **Screen color** from the Simulink **Format** menu. To set the background color of a block or annotation or group of such items, first select the item or items. Then select **Background color** from the Simulink **Format** menu. To set the foreground color of a block or annotation, first select the item. Then select **Foreground color** from the Simulink **Format** menu.

In all cases, Simulink displays a menu of color choices. Choose the desired color from the menu. If you select a color other than **Custom**, Simulink changes the background or foreground color of the diagram or diagram element to the selected color.

Choosing a Custom Color

If you choose **Custom**, Simulink displays the Simulink **Choose Custom Color** dialog box.

The dialog box displays a palette of basic colors and a palette of custom colors that you previously defined. If you have not previously created any custom colors, the custom color palette is all white. To choose a color from either palette, click the color, and then click the **OK** button.

Defining a Custom Color

To define a custom color, click the **Define Custom Colors** button on the **Choose Custom Color** dialog box. The dialog box expands to display a custom color definer.

Hue-saturation cursor

Luminescence cursor

The color definer allows you to specify a custom color by

- Entering the red, green, and blue components of the color as values between 0 (darkest) and 255 (brightest)
- Entering hue, saturation, and luminescence components of the color as values in the range 0 to 255
- Moving the hue-saturation cursor to select the hue and saturation of the desired color and the luminescence cursor to select the luminescence of the desired color

The color that you have defined in any of these ways appears in the **Color|Solid** box. To redefine a color in the **Custom colors** palette, select the color and define a new color, using the color definer. Then click the **Add to Custom Colors** button on the color definer.

Specifying Colors Programmatically

You can use the set_param command at the MATLAB command line or in an M-file program to set parameters that determine the background color of a diagram and the background color and foreground color of diagram elements.

The following table summarizes the parameters that control block diagram colors.

Parameter	Determines
ScreenColor	Background color of block diagram
BackgroundColor	Background color of blocks and annotations
ForegroundColor	Foreground color of blocks and annotations

You can set these parameters to any of the following values:

- 'black', 'white', 'red', 'green', 'blue', 'cyan', 'magenta', 'yellow', 'gray', 'lightBlue', 'orange', 'darkGreen'
- '[r,g,b]'

  where r, g, and b are the red, green, and blue components of the color normalized to the range 0.0 to 1.0.

For example, the following command sets the background color of the currently selected system or subsystem to a light green color:

```
set_param(gcs, 'ScreenColor', '[0.3, 0.9, 0.5]')
```

Enabling Sample Time Colors

Simulink can color code the blocks and lines in your model to indicate the sample rates at which the blocks operate.

Color	Use
Black	Continuous blocks
Magenta	Constant blocks
Yellow	Hybrid (subsystems grouping blocks, or Mux or Demux blocks grouping signals with varying sample times)
Red	Fastest discrete sample time
Green	Second fastest discrete sample time

Color	Use
Blue	Third fastest discrete sample time
Light Blue	Fourth fastest discrete sample time
Dark Green	Fifth fastest discrete sample time
Orange	Sixth fastest discrete sample time
Cyan	Blocks in triggered subsystems
Gray	Fixed in minor step

To enable the sample time colors feature, select **Sample Time Colors** from the **Format** menu.

Simulink does not automatically recolor the model with each change you make to it, so you must select **Update Diagram** from the **Edit** menu to explicitly update the model coloration. To return to your original coloring, disable sample time coloration by again choosing **Sample Time Colors**.

When you use sample time colors, the color assigned to each block depends on its sample time with respect to other sample times in the model.

It is important to note that Mux and Demux blocks are simply grouping operators; signals passing through them retain their timing information. For this reason, the lines emanating from a Demux block can have different colors if they are driven by sources having different sample times. In this case, the Mux and Demux blocks are color coded as hybrids (yellow) to indicate that they handle signals with multiple rates.

Similarly, Subsystem blocks that contain blocks with differing sample times are also colored as hybrids, because there is no single rate associated with them. If all the blocks within a subsystem run at a single rate, the Subsystem block is colored according to that rate.

Connecting Blocks

Simulink block diagrams use lines to represent pathways for signals among blocks in a model (see "Annotating Diagrams" on page 5-16 for information on signals). Simulink can connect blocks for you or you can connect the blocks yourself by drawing lines from their output ports to their input ports.

Automatically Connecting Blocks

You can command Simulink to connect blocks automatically. This eliminates the need for you to draw the connecting lines yourself. When connecting blocks, Simulink routes lines around intervening blocks to avoid cluttering the diagram.

Connecting Two Blocks

To autoconnect two blocks:

1 Select the source block.

2 Hold down **Ctrl** and left-click the destination block.

Simulink connects the source block to the destination block, routing the line around intervening blocks if necessary.

When connecting two blocks, Simulink draws as many connections as possible between the two blocks as illustrated in the following example.

Before autoconnect   After autoconnect

Connecting Groups of Blocks

Simulink can connect a group of source blocks to a destination block or a source block to a group of destination blocks.

To connect a group of source blocks to a destination block:

1 Select the source blocks.

2 Hold down **Ctrl** and left-click the destination block.

To connect a source block to a group of destination blocks:

1 Select the *destination* blocks.

2 Hold down **Ctrl** and left-click the *source* block.

Manually Connecting Blocks

Simulink allows you to draw lines manually between blocks or between lines and blocks. You might want to do this if you need to control the path of the line or to create a branch line.

Drawing a Line Between Blocks

To connect the output port of one block to the input port of another block:

1 Position the cursor over the first block's output port. It is not necessary to position the cursor precisely on the port. The cursor shape changes to crosshairs.

2 Press and hold down the mouse button.

3 Drag the pointer to the second block's input port. You can position the cursor on or near the port or in the block. If you position the cursor in the block, the line is connected to the closest input port. The cursor shape changes to double crosshairs.

4 Release the mouse button. Simulink replaces the port symbols by a connecting line with an arrow showing the direction of the signal flow. You can create lines either from output to input, or from input to output. The arrow is drawn at the appropriate input port, and the signal is the same.

Simulink draws connecting lines using horizontal and vertical line segments. To draw a diagonal line, hold down the **Shift** key while drawing the line.

Drawing a Branch Line

A *branch line* is a line that starts from an existing line and carries its signal to the input port of a block. Both the existing line and the branch line carry the same signal. Using branch lines enables you to cause one signal to be carried to more than one block.

In this example, the output of the Product block goes to both the Scope block and the To Workspace block.

To add a branch line, follow these steps:

1 Position the pointer on the line where you want the branch line to start.

2 While holding down the **Ctrl** key, press and hold down the left mouse button.

3 Drag the pointer to the input port of the target block, then release the mouse button and the **Ctrl** key.

You can also use the right mouse button instead of holding down the left mouse button and the **Ctrl** key.

Drawing a Line Segment

You might want to draw a line with segments exactly where you want them instead of where Simulink draws them. Or you might want to draw a line before you copy the block to which the line is connected. You can do either by drawing line segments.

To draw a line segment, you draw a line that ends in an unoccupied area of the diagram. An arrow appears on the unconnected end of the line. To add another line segment, position the cursor over the end of the segment and draw another segment. Simulink draws the segments as horizontal and vertical lines. To draw diagonal line segments, hold down the **Shift** key while you draw the lines.

Moving a Line Segment

To move a line segment, follow these steps:

1 Position the pointer on the segment you want to move.

2 Press and hold down the left mouse button.

3 Drag the pointer to the desired location.

4 Release the mouse button.

To move the segment connected to an input port, position the pointer over the port and drag the end of the segment to the new location. You cannot move the segment connected to an output port.

Moving a Line Vertex

To move a vertex of a line, follow these steps:

1 Position the pointer on the vertex, then press and hold down the mouse button. The cursor changes to a circle that encloses the vertex.

2 Drag the pointer to the desired location.

3 Release the mouse button.

Inserting Blocks in a Line

You can insert a block in a line by dropping the block on the line. Simulink inserts the block for you at the point where you drop the block. The block that you insert can have only one input and one output.

To insert a block in a line:

1 Position the pointer over the block and press the left mouse button.

2 Drag the block over the line in which you want to insert the block.

3 Release the mouse button to drop the block on the line. Simulink inserts the block where you dropped it.

Disconnecting Blocks

To disconnect a block from its connecting lines, hold down the **Shift** key, then drag the block to a new location.

Annotating Diagrams

Annotations provide textual information about a model. You can add an annotation to any unoccupied area of your block diagram.

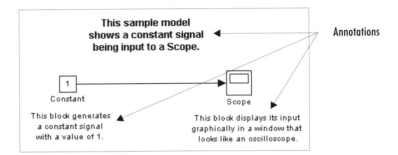

To create a model annotation, double-click an unoccupied area of the block diagram. A small rectangle appears and the cursor changes to an insertion point. Start typing the annotation contents. Each line is centered within the rectangle that surrounds the annotation.

To move an annotation, drag it to a new location.

To edit an annotation, select it:

- To replace the annotation, click the annotation, then double-click or drag the cursor to select it. Then, enter the new annotation.
- To insert characters, click between two characters to position the insertion point, then insert text.
- To replace characters, drag the mouse to select a range of text to replace, then enter the new text.

To delete an annotation, hold down the **Shift** key while you select the annotation, then press the **Delete** or **Backspace** key.

To change the font of all or part of an annotation, select the text in the annotation you want to change, then choose **Font** from the **Format** menu. Select a font and size from the dialog box.

To change the text alignment (e.g., left, center, or right) of the annotation, select the annotation and choose **Text Alignment** from the model window's

Format or context menu. Then choose one of the alignment options (e.g., Center) from the Text Alignment submenu.

Using TeX Formatting Commands in Annotations

You can use TeX formatting commands to include mathematical and other symbols and Greek letters in block diagram annotations.

To use TeX commands in an annotation:

1 Select the annotation.

2 Select Enable TeX Commands from the Edit menu on the model window.

3 Enter or edit the text of the annotation, using TeX commands where needed to achieve the desired appearance.

See "Mathematical Symbols, Greek Letters, and TeX Characters" in the MATLAB documentation for information on the TeX formatting commands supported by Simulink.

4 Deselect the annotation by clicking outside it or typing **Esc**.

Simulink displays the formatted text.

Creating Subsystems

As your model increases in size and complexity, you can simplify it by grouping blocks into subsystems. Using subsystems has these advantages:

- It helps reduce the number of blocks displayed in your model window.
- It allows you to keep functionally related blocks together.
- It enables you to establish a hierarchical block diagram, where a Subsystem block is on one layer and the blocks that make up the subsystem are on another.

You can create a subsystem in two ways:

- Add a Subsystem block to your model, then open that block and add the blocks it contains to the subsystem window.
- Add the blocks that make up the subsystem, then group those blocks into a subsystem.

Creating a Subsystem by Adding the Subsystem Block

To create a subsystem before adding the blocks it contains, add a Subsystem block to the model, then add the blocks that make up the subsystem:

1 Copy the Subsystem block from the Signals & Systems library into your model.

2 Open the Subsystem block by double-clicking it.

Simulink opens the subsystem in the current or a new model window, depending on the model window reuse mode that you selected (see "Window Reuse" on page 5-22).

3 In the empty Subsystem window, create the subsystem. Use Inport blocks to represent input from outside the subsystem and Outport blocks to represent external output.

For example, the subsystem shown includes a Sum block and Inport and Outport blocks to represent input to and output from the subsystem.

Creating a Subsystem by Grouping Existing Blocks

If your model already contains the blocks you want to convert to a subsystem, you can create the subsystem by grouping those blocks:

1 Enclose the blocks and connecting lines that you want to include in the subsystem within a bounding box. You cannot specify the blocks to be grouped by selecting them individually or by using the **Select All** command. For more information, see "Selecting Multiple Objects Using a Bounding Box" on page 5-3.

For example, this figure shows a model that represents a counter. The Sum and Unit Delay blocks are selected within a bounding box.

When you release the mouse button, the two blocks and all the connecting lines are selected.

2 Choose **Create Subsystem** from the **Edit** menu. Simulink replaces the selected blocks with a Subsystem block.

This figure shows the model after you choose the **Create Subsystem** command (and resize the Subsystem block so the port labels are readable).

If you open the Subsystem block, Simulink displays the underlying system, as shown below. Notice that Simulink adds Inport and Outport blocks to represent input from and output to blocks outside the subsystem.

As with all blocks, you can change the name of the Subsystem block. You can also customize the icon and dialog box for the block using the masking feature, described in Chapter 10, "Creating Masked Subsystems."

Undoing Subsystem Creation

To undo creation of a subsystem by grouping blocks, select **Undo** from the **Edit** menu. You can undo creation of a subsystem that you have subsequently edited. However, the **Undo** command does not undo any nongraphical changes that you made to the blocks, such as changing the value of a block parameter or the name of a block. Simulink alerts you to this limitation by displaying a warning dialog box before undoing creation of a modified subsystem.

Model Navigation Commands

Subsystems allow you to create a hierarchical model comprising many layers. You can navigate this hierarchy, using the Simulink Model Browser (see "The Model Browser" on page 9-8) and/or the following model navigation commands:

- **Open**

  The **Open** command opens the currently selected subsystem. To execute the command, choose **Open** from the Simulink **Edit** menu, press **Enter**, or double-click the subsystem.

- **Open block in new window**

  Opens the currently selected subsystem regardless of Simulink's window reuse settings (see "Window Reuse" on page 5-22).

- **Go to Parent**

  The **Go to Parent** command displays the parent of the subsystem displayed in the current window. To execute the command, press **Esc** or select **Go to Parent** from the Simulink **View** menu.

Window Reuse

You can specify whether Simulink's model navigation commands use the current window or a new window to display a subsystem or its parent. Reusing windows avoids cluttering your screen with windows. Creating a window for each subsystem allows you to view subsystems side by side with their parents or siblings. To specify your preference regarding window reuse, select **Preferences** from the Simulink **File** menu and then select one of the following **Window reuse type** options listed in the Simulink **Preferences** dialog box.

Reuse Type	Open Action	Go to Parent (Esc) Action
none	Subsystem appears in a new window.	Parent window moves to the front.
reuse	Subsystem replaces the parent in the current window.	Parent window replaces subsystem in current window

Reuse Type	Open Action	Go to Parent (Esc) Action
replace	Subsystem appears in a new window. Parent window disappears.	Parent window appears. Subsystem window disappears.
mixed	Subsystem appears in its own window.	Parent window rises to front. Subsystem window disappears.

Labeling Subsystem Ports

Simulink labels ports on a Subsystem block. The labels are the names of Inport and Outport blocks that connect the subsystem to blocks outside the subsystem through these ports.

You can hide (or show) the port labels by

- Selecting the Subsystem block, then choosing **Hide Port Labels** (or **Show Port Labels**) from the **Format** menu
- Selecting an Inport or Outport block in the subsystem and choosing **Hide Name** (or **Show Name**) from the **Format** menu
- Selecting the **Show port labels** option in the Subsystem block's parameter dialog

This figure shows two models. The subsystem on the left contains two Inport blocks and one Outport block. The Subsystem block on the right shows the labeled ports.

Subsystem with Inport and Outport blocks   Subsystem with labeled ports

Controlling Access to Subsystems

Simulink allows you to control user access to subsystems that reside in libraries. In particular, you can prevent a user from viewing or modifying the contents of a library subsystem while still allowing the user to employ the subsystem in a model.

To control access to a library subsystem, open the subsystem's parameter dialog box and set its Access parameter to either ReadOnly or NoReadOrWrite. The first option allows a user to view the contents of the library subsystem and make local copies but prevents the user from modifying the original library copy. The second option prevents the user from viewing the contents of, creating local copies, or modifying the permissions of the library subsystem. See the Subsystem block for more information on subsystem access options. Note that both options allow a user to use the library system in models by creating links (see "Working with Block Libraries" on page 6-25).

Creating Conditionally Executed Subsystems

A *conditionally executed subsystem* is a subsystem whose execution depends on the value of an input signal. The signal that controls whether a subsystem executes is called the *control signal*. The signal enters the Subsystem block at the *control input*.

Conditionally executed subsystems can be very useful when you are building complex models that contain components whose execution depends on other components.

Simulink supports three types of conditionally executed subsystems:

- An *enabled subsystem* executes while the control signal is positive. It starts execution at the time step where the control signal crosses zero (from the negative to the positive direction) and continues execution while the control signal remains positive. Enabled subsystems are described in more detail in "Enabled Subsystems" on page 5-25.

- A *triggered subsystem* executes once each time a trigger event occurs. A trigger event can occur on the rising or falling edge of a trigger signal, which can be continuous or discrete. Triggered subsystems are described in more detail in "Triggered Subsystems" on page 5-30.

- A *triggered and enabled subsystem* executes once on the time step when a trigger event occurs if the enable control signal has a positive value at that step. See "Triggered and Enabled Subsystems" on page 5-33 for more information.

- A *control flow statement* executes C-like control flow logic under the supervision of a control flow block. In all cases, the blocks executed reside in a controlled subsystem. In the case of `if-else` and `switch` control flow, the control block resides outside the controlled subsystem and issues a control signal to an Action Port block residing inside the controlled subsystem. In the case of `while`, `do-while`, and `for` control flow, a block with iterative control resides inside the subsystem, which it controls without an apparent control signal. See "Control Flow Blocks" on page 5-37 for more information.

Enabled Subsystems

Enabled subsystems are subsystems that execute at each simulation step where the control signal has a positive value.

An enabled subsystem has a single control input, which can be scalar or vector valued:

- If the input is a scalar, the subsystem executes if the input value is greater than zero.
- If the input is a vector, the subsystem executes if *any* of the vector elements is greater than zero.

For example, if the control input signal is a sine wave, the subsystem is alternately enabled and disabled, as shown in this figure. An up arrow signifies enable, a down arrow disable.

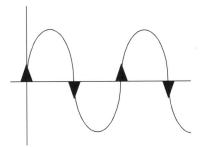

Simulink uses the zero-crossing slope method to determine whether an enable is to occur. If the signal crosses zero and the slope is positive, the subsystem is enabled. If the slope is negative at the zero crossing, the subsystem is disabled.

Creating an Enabled Subsystem

You create an enabled subsystem by copying an Enable block from the Signals & Systems library into a subsystem. Simulink adds an enable symbol and an enable control input port to the Subsystem block icon.

Subsystem

Setting Output Values While the Subsystem Is Disabled. Although an enabled subsystem does not execute while it is disabled, the output signal is still available to other blocks. While an enabled subsystem is disabled, you can choose to hold the subsystem outputs at their previous values or reset them to their initial conditions.

Open each Outport block's dialog box and select one of the choices for the **Output when disabled** parameter, as shown in the dialog box following:

- Choose held to cause the output to maintain its most recent value.
- Choose reset to cause the output to revert to its initial condition. Set the **Initial output** to the initial value of the output.

Select an option to set the Outport output while the subsystem is disabled.

The initial condition and the value when reset.

Setting States When the Subsystem Becomes Reenabled. When an enabled subsystem executes, you can choose whether to hold the subsystem states at their previous values or reset them to their initial conditions.

To do this, open the Enable block dialog box and select one of the choices for the **States when enabling** parameter, as shown in the dialog box following:

- Choose held to cause the states to maintain their most recent values.
- Choose reset to cause the states to revert to their initial conditions.

Select an option to set the states when the subsystem is reenabled.

Outputting the Enable Control Signal. An option on the Enable block dialog box lets you output the enable control signal. To output the control signal, select the **Show output port** check box.

This feature allows you to pass the control signal down into the enabled subsystem, which can be useful where logic within the enabled subsystem is dependent on the value or values contained in the control signal.

Blocks an Enabled Subsystem Can Contain

An enabled subsystem can contain any block, whether continuous or discrete. Discrete blocks in an enabled subsystem execute only when the subsystem executes, and only when their sample times are synchronized with the simulation sample time. Enabled subsystems and the model use a common clock.

Note Enabled subsystems can contain Goto blocks. However, only state ports can connect to Goto blocks in an enabled subsystem. See the Simulink demo model, `clutch`, for an example of how to use Goto blocks in an enabled subsystem.

For example, this system contains four discrete blocks and a control signal. The discrete blocks are

- Block A, which has a sample time of 0.25 second
- Block B, which has a sample time of 0.5 second
- Block C, within the enabled subsystem, which has a sample time of 0.125 second
- Block D, also within the enabled subsystem, which has a sample time of 0.25 second

The enable control signal is generated by a Pulse Generator block, labeled Signal E, which changes from 0 to 1 at 0.375 second and returns to 0 at 0.875 second.

The chart below indicates when the discrete blocks execute.

Blocks A and B execute independently of the enable control signal because they are not part of the enabled subsystem. When the enable control signal becomes positive, blocks C and D execute at their assigned sample rates until the enable control signal becomes zero again. Note that block C does not execute at 0.875 second when the enable control signal changes to zero.

Triggered Subsystems

Triggered subsystems are subsystems that execute each time a trigger event occurs.

A triggered subsystem has a single control input, called the *trigger input*, that determines whether the subsystem executes. You can choose from three types of trigger events to force a triggered subsystem to begin execution:

- rising triggers execution of the subsystem when the control signal rises from a negative or zero value to a positive value (or zero if the initial value is negative).

- falling triggers execution of the subsystem when the control signal falls from a positive or a zero value to a negative value (or zero if the initial value is positive).

- either triggers execution of the subsystem when the signal is either rising or falling.

Note In the case of discrete systems, a signal's rising or falling from zero is considered a trigger event only if the signal has remained at zero for more than one time step preceding the rise or fall. This eliminates false triggers caused by control signal sampling.

For example, in the following timing diagram for a discrete system, a rising trigger (R) does not occur at time step 3 because the signal has remained at zero for only one time step when the rise occurs.

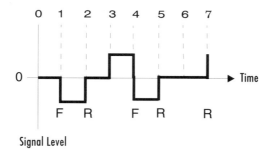

Signal Level

A simple example of a triggered subsystem is illustrated.

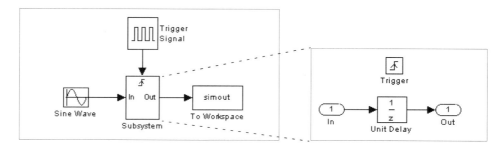

In this example, the subsystem is triggered on the rising edge of the square wave trigger control signal.

Creating a Triggered Subsystem

You create a triggered subsystem by copying the Trigger block from the Signals & Systems library into a subsystem. Simulink adds a trigger symbol and a trigger control input port to the Subsystem block icon.

To select the trigger type, open the Trigger block dialog box and select one of the choices for the **Trigger type** parameter, as shown in the dialog box following:

Select the trigger type from these choices.

Simulink uses different symbols on the Trigger and Subsystem blocks to indicate rising and falling triggers (or either). This figure shows the trigger symbols on Subsystem blocks.

Subsystem with Rising trigger   Subsystem with Falling trigger   Subsystem with Rising or Falling trigger

Outputs and States Between Trigger Events. Unlike enabled subsystems, triggered subsystems always hold their outputs at the last value between triggering events. Also, triggered subsystems cannot reset their states when triggered; states of any discrete blocks are held between trigger events.

Outputting the Trigger Control Signal. An option on the Trigger block dialog box lets you output the trigger control signal. To output the control signal, select the **Show output port** check box.

Select this check box to show the output port.

The **Output data type** field allows you to specify the data type of the output signal as auto, int8, or double. The auto option causes the data type of the output signal to be set to the data type (either `int8` or `double`) of the port to which the signal is connected.

Function-Call Subsystems

You can create a triggered subsystem whose execution is determined by logic internal to an S-function instead of by the value of a signal. These subsystems are called *function-call subsystems*. For more information about function-call subsystems, see "Function-Call Subsystems" in the "Implementing Block Features" section of *Writing S-Functions*.

Blocks That a Triggered Subsystem Can Contain

Triggered systems execute only at specific times during a simulation. As a result, the only blocks that are suitable for use in a triggered subsystem are

- Blocks with inherited sample time, such as the Logical Operator block or the Gain block
- Discrete blocks having their sample times set to -1, which indicates that the sample time is inherited from the driving block

Triggered and Enabled Subsystems

A third kind of conditionally executed subsystem combines both types of conditional execution. The behavior of this type of subsystem, called a *triggered and enabled* subsystem, is a combination of the enabled subsystem and the triggered subsystem, as shown by this flow diagram.

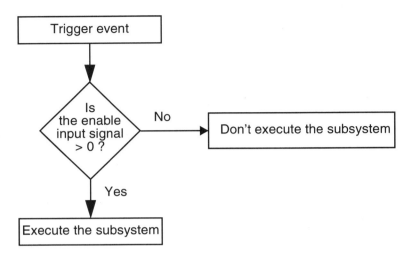

A triggered and enabled subsystem contains both an enable input port and a trigger input port. When the trigger event occurs, Simulink checks the enable input port to evaluate the enable control signal. If its value is greater than zero, Simulink executes the subsystem. If both inputs are vectors, the subsystem executes if at least one element of each vector is nonzero.

The subsystem executes once at the time step at which the trigger event occurs.

Creating a Triggered and Enabled Subsystem

You create a triggered and enabled subsystem by dragging both the Enable and Trigger blocks from the Signals & Systems library into an existing subsystem. Simulink adds enable and trigger symbols and enable and trigger and enable control inputs to the Subsystem block icon.

You can set output values when a triggered and enabled subsystem is disabled as you would for an enabled subsystem. For more information, see "Setting Output Values While the Subsystem Is Disabled" on page 5-26. Also, you can specify what the values of the states are when the subsystem is reenabled. See "Setting States When the Subsystem Becomes Reenabled" on page 5-27.

Set the parameters for the Enable and Trigger blocks separately. The procedures are the same as those described for the individual blocks.

A Sample Triggered and Enabled Subsystem

A simple example of a triggered and enabled subsystem is illustrated in the model below.

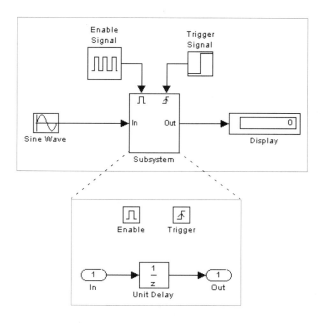

Creating Alternately Executing Subsystems

You can use conditionally executed subsystems in combination with Merge blocks to create sets of subsystems that execute alternately, depending on the current state of the model. For example, the following figure shows a model that uses two enabled blocks and a Merge block to model an inverter, that is, a device that converts AC current to pulsating DC current.

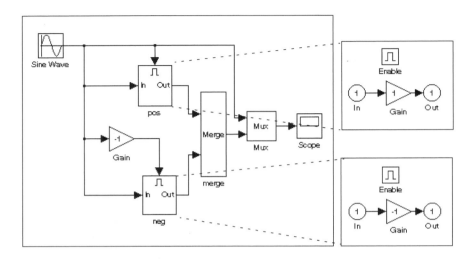

In this example, the block labeled "pos" is enabled when the AC waveform is positive; it passes the waveform unchanged to its output. The block labeled "neg" is enabled when the waveform is negative; it inverts the waveform. The Merge block passes the output of the currently enabled block to the Mux block, which passes the output, along with the original waveform, to the Scope block.

The Scope creates the following display.

Control Flow Blocks

The control flow blocks are used to implement the logic of the following C-like control flow statements in Simulink:

- `for`
- `if-else`
- `switch`
- `while` (includes `while` and `do-while` control flow statements)

Although all the preceding control flow statements are implementable in Stateflow, these blocks are intended to provide Simulink users with tools that meet their needs for simpler logical requirements.

Creating Conditional Control Flow Statements

You create C-like conditional control flow statements using ordinary subsystems and the following blocks from the Subsystems library.

C Statement	Blocks Used
`if-else`	If, Action Port
`switch`	Switch Case, Action Port

If-Else Control Flow Statements. The following diagram depicts a generalized `if-else` control flow statement implementation in Simulink.

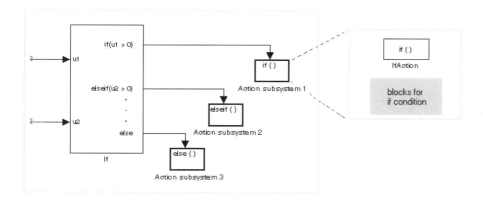

Construct a Simulink `if-else` control flow statement as follows:

- Provide data inputs to the If block for constructing if-else conditions.

  Inputs to the If block are set in the If block properties dialog. Internally, they are designated as `u1`, `u2`,`...`, `un` and are used to construct output conditions.

- Set output port if-else conditions for the If block.

  Output ports for the If block are also set in its properties dialog. You use the input values `u1`, `u2`, `...`, `un` to express conditions for the if, elseif, and else condition fields in the dialog. Of these, only the if field is required. You can enter multiple elseif conditions and select a check box to enable the else condition.

- Connect each condition output port to an Action subsystem.

  Each if, elseif, and else condition output port on the If block is connected to a subsystem to be executed if the port's case is true. You create these subsystems by placing an Action Port block in a subsystem. This creates an atomic Action subsystem with a port named Action, which you then connect to a condition on the If block. Once connected, the subsystem takes on the identity of the condition it is connected to and behaves like an enabled subsystem.

For more detailed information, see the reference topics for the If and Action Port blocks.

Note All blocks in an Action subsystem driven by an If or Switch Case block must run at the same rate as the driving block.

Switch Control Flow Statements. The following diagram depicts a generalized switch control flow statement implementation in Simulink.

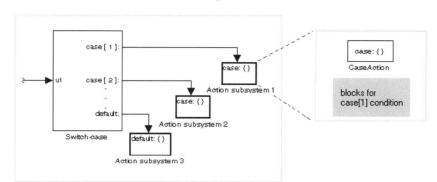

Construct a Simulink switch control flow statement as follows:

- Provide a data input to the argument input of the Switch Case block.

  The input to the Switch Case block is the argument to the switch control flow statement. This value determines the appropriate case to execute. Noninteger inputs to this port are truncated.

- Add cases to the Switch Case block based on the numeric value of the argument input.

  You add cases to the Switch Case block through the properties dialog of the Switch Case block. Cases can be single or multivalued. You can also add an optional default case, which is true if no other cases are true. Once added, these cases appear as output ports on the Switch Case block.

- Connect each Switch Case block case output port to an Action subsystem.

  Each case output of the Switch Case block is connected to a subsystem to be executed if the port's case is true. You create these subsystems by placing an Action Port block in a subsystem. This creates an atomic subsystem with a port named Action, which you then connect to a condition on the Switch Case block. Once connected, the subsystem takes on the identity of the condition and behaves like an enabled subsystem. Place all the block programming executed for that case in this subsystem.

For more detailed information, see the reference topics for the Switch Case and Action Port blocks.

Note After the subsystem for a particular case is executed, an implied break is executed that exits the switch control flow statement altogether. Simulink switch control flow statement implementations do not exhibit "fall through" behavior like C switch statements.

Creating Iterator Control Flow Statements

You create C-like iterator control flow statements using subsystems and the following blocks from the Subsystems library.

C Statement	Blocks Used
do-while	While Iterator
for	For Iterator
while	While Iterator

While Control Flow Statements

The following diagram depicts a generalized C-like while control flow statement implementation in Simulink.

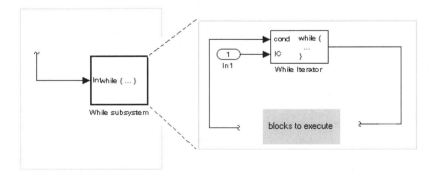

In a Simulink while control flow statement, the While Iterator block iterates the contents of a While subsystem, an atomic subsystem. For each iteration of the While Iterator block, the block programming of the While subsystem executes one complete path through its blocks.

Construct a Simulink `while` control flow statement as follows:

- Place a While Iterator block in a subsystem.

  The host subsystem becomes a `while` control flow statement as indicated by its new label, `while {...}`. These subsystems behave like triggered subsystems. This subsystem is host to the block programming you want to iterate with the While Iterator block.

- Provide a data input for the initial condition data input port of the While Iterator block.

  The While Iterator block requires an initial condition data input (labeled `IC`) for its first iteration. This must originate outside the While subsystem. If this value is nonzero, the first iteration takes place.

- Provide data input for the conditions port of the While Iterator block.

  Conditions for the remaining iterations are passed to the data input port labeled `cond`. Input for this port must originate inside the While subsystem.

- You can set the While Iterator block to output its iterator value through its properties dialog.

  The iterator value is 1 for the first iteration and is incremented by 1 for each succeeding iteration.

- You can change the iteration of the While Iterator block to `do-while` through its properties dialog.

  This changes the label of the host subsystem to `do {...} while`. With a `do-while` iteration, the While Iteration block no longer has an initial condition (IC) port, because all blocks in the subsystem are executed once before the condition port (labeled `cond`) is checked.

For specific details, see the reference topic for the While Iterator block.

For Control Flow Statements. The following diagram depicts a generalized `for` control flow statement implementation in Simulink.

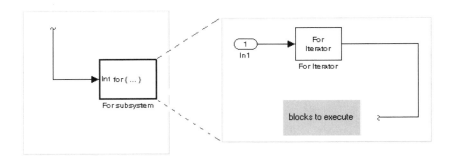

In a Simulink `for` control flow statement, the For Iterator block iterates the contents of a For Iterator Subsystem, an atomic subsystem. For each iteration of the For Iterator block, the block programming of the For Iterator Subsystem executes one complete path through its blocks.

Construct a Simulink `for` control flow statement as follows:

- Drag a For Iterator Subsystem block from the Library Browser or Library window into your model.

- You can set the For Iterator block to take external or internal input for the number of iterations it executes.

  Through the properties dialog of the For Iterator block you can set it to take input for the number of iterations through the port labeled N. This input must come from outside the For Iterator Subsystem.

  You can also set the number of iterations directly in the properties dialog.

- You can set the For Iterator block to output its iterator value for use in the block programming of the For Iterator Subsystem.

  The iterator value is 1 for the first iteration and is incremented by 1 for each succeeding iteration.

The For Iterator block works well with the Assignment block to reassign values in a vector or matrix. This is demonstrated in the following example. Note the matrix dimensions in the data being passed.

The above example outputs the sin value of an input 2-by-5 matrix (2 rows, 5 columns) using a For subsystem containing an Assignment block. The process is as follows:

1 A 2-by-5 matrix is input to the Selector block and the Assignment block.

2 The Selector block strips off a 2-by-1 matrix from the input matrix at the column value indicated by the current iteration value of the For Iterator block.

3 The sine of the 2-by-1 matrix is taken.

4 The sine value 2-by-1 matrix is passed to an Assignment block.

5 The Assignment block, which takes the original 2-by-5 matrix as one of its inputs, assigns the 2-by-1 matrix back into the original matrix at the column location indicated by the iteration value.

The rows specified for reassignment in the property dialog for the Assignment block in the above example are [1,2]. Because there are only two rows in the original matrix, you could also have specified -1 for the rows, i.e., all rows.

Note Experienced Simulink users will note that the sin block is already capable of taking the sine of a matrix. The above example uses the sin block only as an example of changing each element of a matrix with the collaboration of an Assignment block and a For Iterator block.

Comparing Stateflow and Control Flow Statements

Stateflow already possesses the logical capabilities of the Simulink control flow statements. It can call Function-Call subsystems (see "Function-Call Subsystems" on page 5-33) on condition or iteratively. However, since Stateflow provides a great deal more in logical sophistication, if your requirements are simpler, you might find the capabilities of the Simulink control flow blocks sufficient for your needs. In addition, the control flow statements offer a few advantages, which are listed in the following topics.

Sample Times. The Function-Call subsystems that Stateflow can call are triggered subsystems. Triggered subsystems inherit their sample times from the calling block. However, the Action subsystems used in if-else and switch control flow statements and the While and For subsystems that make up while and for control flow statements are enabled subsystems. Enabled subsystems can have their own sample times independent of the calling block. This also allows you to use more categories of blocks in your iterated subsystem than in a Function-Call subsystem.

Resetting of States When Reenabled. Simulink control flow statement blocks allow you to retain or reset (to their initial values) the values of states for Action, For, and While subsystems when they are reenabled. For detailed information, see the references for the While Iterator and For Iterator blocks regarding the parameter **States when starting** and the reference for the Action Port block regarding the parameter **States when execution is resumed**.

Using Stateflow with the Control Flow Blocks

You might want to consider the possibility of using Stateflow and the Simulink control flow blocks together. The following sections contain some examples that give you a few suggestions on how to combine the two.

Using Stateflow with If-Else or Switch Subsystems. In the following model, Stateflow places one of a variety of values in a Stateflow data object. Upon chart termination, a Simulink `if` control flow statement uses that data to make a conditional decision.

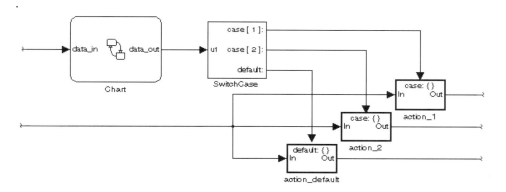

In this case, control is given to a Switch Case block, which uses the value to choose one of several case subsystems to execute.

Using Stateflow with While Subsystems. In the following diagram, Stateflow computes the value of a data object that is available to a condition input of a While Iterator block in do-while mode.

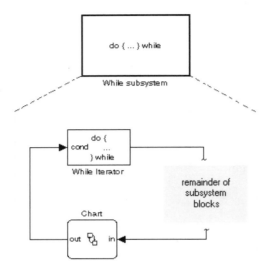

The While Iterator block has iterative control over its host subsystem, which includes the Stateflow Chart block. In do-while mode, the While block is guaranteed to operate for its first iteration value (= 1). During that time, the Stateflow chart is awakened and sets a data value used by the While Iterator block, which is evaluated as a condition for the next while iteration.

In the following diagram, the While block is now set in while mode. In this mode, the While Iterator block must have input to its initial condition port in order to execute its first iteration value. This value must come from outside the While subsystem.

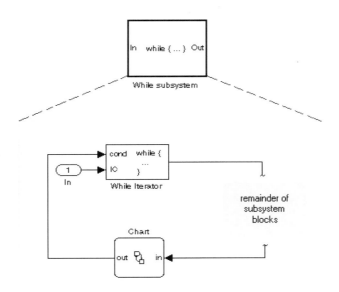

If the initial condition is true, the While Iterator block wakes up the Stateflow chart and executes it to termination. During that time the Stateflow chart sets data, which the While Iterator condition port uses as a condition for the next iteration.

Using Callback Routines

You can define MATLAB expressions that execute when the block diagram or a block is acted upon in a particular way. These expressions, called *callback routines*, are associated with block, port, or model parameters. For example, the callback associated with a block's OpenFcn parameter is executed when the model user double-clicks on that block's name or the path changes.

Tracing Callbacks

Callback tracing allows you to determine the callbacks Simulink invokes and in what order Simulink invokes them when you open or simulate a model. To enable callback tracing, select the **Callback tracing** option on the Simulink **Preferences** dialog box (see "Setting Simulink Preferences" on page 2-16) or execute set_param(0, 'CallbackTracing', 'on'). This option causes Simulink to list callbacks in the MATLAB Command Window as they are invoked.

Creating Model Callback Functions

You can create model callback functions interactively or programmatically. Use the **Callbacks** pane of the model's **Model Properties** dialog box to create model callbacks interactively. To create a callback programmatically, use the set_param command to assign a MATLAB expression that implements the function to the model parameter corresponding to the callback (see "Model Callback Parameters" on page 5-49).

For example, this command evaluates the variable testvar when the user double-clicks the Test block in mymodel.

```
set_param('mymodel/Test', 'OpenFcn', testvar)
```

You can examine the clutch system (clutch.mdl) for routines associated with many model callbacks.

Model Callback Parameters

The following table lists the model parameters used to specify model callback routines and indicates when the corresponding callback routines are executed.

Parameter	When Executed
CloseFcn	Before the block diagram is closed.
PostLoadFcn	After the model is loaded. Defining a callback routine for this parameter might be useful for generating an interface that requires that the model has already been loaded.
InitFcn	Called at start of model simulation.
PostSaveFcn	After the model is saved.
PreLoadFcn	Before the model is loaded. Defining a callback routine for this parameter might be useful for loading variables used by the model.
PreSaveFcn	Before the model is saved.
StartFcn	Before the simulation starts.
StopFcn	After the simulation stops. Output is written to workspace variables and files before the StopFcn is executed.

Creating Block Callback Functions

You can create model callback functions interactively or programmatically. Use the **Callbacks** pane of the model's **Block Properties** dialog box (see "Callbacks Pane" on page 6-10) to create model callbacks interactively. To create a callback programmatically, use the set_param command to assign a MATLAB expression that implements the function to the block parameter corresponding to the callback (see "Block Callback Parameters" on page 5-50).

Note A callback for a masked subsystem cannot directly reference the parameters of the masked subsystem (see "About Masks" on page 10-2). The reason? Simulink evaluates block callbacks in a model's base workspace whereas the mask parameters reside in the masked subsystem's private workspace. A block callback, however, can use get_param to obtain the value of a mask parameter, e.g., get_param(gcb, 'gain'), where gain is the name of a mask parameter of the current block.

Block Callback Parameters

This table lists the parameters for which you can define block callback routines, and indicates when those callback routines are executed. Routines that are executed before or after actions take place occur immediately before or after the action.

Parameter	When Executed
CloseFcn	When the block is closed using the close_system command.
CopyFcn	After a block is copied. The callback is recursive for Subsystem blocks (that is, if you copy a Subsystem block that contains a block for which the CopyFcn parameter is defined, the routine is also executed). The routine is also executed if an add_block command is used to copy the block.
DeleteFcn	Before a block is deleted. This callback is recursive for Subsystem blocks.

Parameter	When Executed
DestroyFcn	When the block has been destroyed.
InitFcn	Before the block diagram is compiled and before block parameters are evaluated.
LoadFcn	After the block diagram is loaded. This callback is recursive for Subsystem blocks.
ModelCloseFcn	Before the block diagram is closed. This callback is recursive for Subsystem blocks.
MoveFcn	When the block is moved or resized.
NameChangeFcn	After a block's name and/or path changes. When a Subsystem block's path is changed, it recursively calls this function for all blocks it contains after calling its own NameChangeFcn routine.
OpenFcn	When the block is opened. This parameter is generally used with Subsystem blocks. The routine is executed when you double-click the block or when an open_system command is called with the block as an argument. The OpenFcn parameter overrides the normal behavior associated with opening a block, which is to display the block's dialog box or to open the subsystem.
ParentCloseFcn	Before closing a subsystem containing the block or when the block is made part of a new subsystem using the new_system command (see new_system in the "Model Creation Commands" section of the Simulink online Help).
PreSaveFcn	Before the block diagram is saved. This callback is recursive for Subsystem blocks.
PostSaveFcn	After the block diagram is saved. This callback is recursive for Subsystem blocks.

Parameter	When Executed
StartFcn	After the block diagram is compiled and before the simulation starts. In the case of an S-Function block, StartFcn executes immediately before the first execution of the block's mdlProcessParameters function. See "S-Function Callback Methods" in *Writing S-Functions* in the Simulink online Help for more information.
StopFcn	At any termination of the simulation. In the case of an S-Function block, StopFcn executes after the block's mdlTerminate function executes. See "S-Function Callback Methods" in *Writing S-Functions* in the Simulink online Help for more information.
UndoDeleteFcn	When a block delete is undone.

Port Callback Parameters

Block input and output ports have a single callback parameter, ConnectionCallback. This parameter allows you to set callbacks on ports that are triggered every time the connectivity of those ports changes. Examples of connectivity changes include deletion of blocks connected to the port and deletion, disconnection, or connection of branches or lines to the port.

Use get_param to get the port handle of a port and set_param to set the callback on the port. For example, suppose the currently selected block has a single input port. The following code fragment sets foo as the connection callback on the input port.

```
phs = get_param(gcb, 'PortHandles');
set_param(phs.Inport, 'ConnectionCallback', 'foo');
```

The first argument of the callback function must be a port handle. The callback function can have other arguments (and a return value) as well. For example, the following is a valid callback function signature.

```
function foo(port, otherArg1, otherArg2)
```

Working with Blocks

This section explores the following block-related topics.

About Blocks

Blocks are the elements from which Simulink models are built. You can model virtually any dynamic system by creating and interconnecting blocks in appropriate ways. This section discusses how to use blocks to build models of dynamic systems.

Block Data Tips

On Microsoft Windows, Simulink displays information about a block in a pop-up window when you allow the pointer to hover over the block in the diagram view. To disable this feature or control what information a data tip includes, select **Block data tips options** from the Simulink **View** menu.

Virtual Blocks

When creating models, you need to be aware that Simulink blocks fall into two basic categories: nonvirtual and virtual blocks. Nonvirtual blocks play an active role in the simulation of a system. If you add or remove a nonvirtual block, you change the model's behavior. Virtual blocks, by contrast, play no active role in the simulation; they help organize a model graphically. Some Simulink blocks are virtual in some circumstances and nonvirtual in others. Such blocks are called conditionally virtual blocks. The following table lists Simulink virtual and conditionally virtual blocks.

Block Name	Condition Under Which Block Is Virtual
Bus Selector	Always virtual.
Demux	Always virtual.
Enable Port	Always virtual.
From	Always virtual.
Goto	Always virtual.
Goto Tag Visibility	Always virtual.
Ground	Always virtual.

Block Name	Condition Under Which Block Is Virtual
Inport	Virtual *unless* the block resides in a conditionally executed subsystem *and* has a direct connection to an outport block.
Mux	Always virtual.
Outport	Virtual when the block resides within any subsystem block (conditional or not), and does *not* reside in the root (top-level) Simulink window.
Selector	Virtual except in matrix mode.
Subsystem	Virtual unless the block is conditionally executed and/or the block's **Treat as Atomic Unit** option is selected.
Terminator	Always virtual.
Trigger Port	Virtual when the outport port is *not* present.

Editing Blocks

The Simulink Editor allows you to cut and paste blocks in and between models.

Copying and Moving Blocks from One Window to Another

As you build your model, you often copy blocks from Simulink block libraries or other libraries or models into your model window. To do this, follow these steps:

1 Open the appropriate block library or model window.

2 Drag the block to copy into the target model window. To drag a block, position the cursor over the block icon, then press and hold down the mouse button. Move the cursor into the target window, then release the mouse button.

You can also drag blocks from the Simulink Library Browser into a model window. See "Browsing Block Libraries" on page 6-31 for more information.

Note Simulink hides the names of Sum, Mux, Demux, Bus Creator, and Bus Selector blocks when you copy them from the Simulink block library to a model. This is done to avoid unnecessarily cluttering the model diagram. (The shapes of these blocks clearly indicate their respective functions.)

You can also copy blocks by using the **Copy** and **Paste** commands from the **Edit** menu:

1 Select the block you want to copy.

2 Choose **Copy** from the **Edit** menu.

3 Make the target model window the active window.

4 Choose **Paste** from the **Edit** menu.

Simulink assigns a name to each copied block. If it is the first block of its type in the model, its name is the same as its name in the source window. For example, if you copy the Gain block from the Math library into your model window, the name of the new block is Gain. If your model already contains a block named Gain, Simulink adds a sequence number to the block name (for example, Gain1, Gain2). You can rename blocks; see "Manipulating Block Names" on page 6-13.

When you copy a block, the new block inherits all the original block's parameter values.

Simulink uses an invisible five-pixel grid to simplify the alignment of blocks. All blocks within a model snap to a line on the grid. You can move a block slightly up, down, left, or right by selecting the block and pressing the arrow keys.

You can display the grid in the model window by typing the following command in the MATLAB window.

```
set_param('<model name>','showgrid','on')
```

To change the grid spacing, enter

```
set_param('<model name>','gridspacing',<number of pixels>)
```

For example, to change the grid spacing to 20 pixels, enter

```
set_param('<model name>','gridspacing',20)
```

For either of the above commands, you can also select the model, then enter gcs instead of <model name>.

You can copy or move blocks to compatible applications (such as word processing programs) using the **Copy**, **Cut**, and **Paste** commands. These commands copy only the graphic representation of the blocks, not their parameters.

Moving blocks from one window to another is similar to copying blocks, except that you hold down the **Shift** key while you select the blocks.

You can use the **Undo** command from the **Edit** menu to remove an added block.

Moving Blocks in a Model

To move a single block from one place to another in a model window, drag the block to a new location. Simulink automatically repositions lines connected to the moved block.

To move more than one block, including connecting lines:

1 Select the blocks and lines. If you need information about how to select more than one block, see "Selecting More Than One Object" on page 5-3.

2 Drag the objects to their new location and release the mouse button.

Copying Blocks in a Model

You can copy blocks in a model as follows. While holding down the **Ctrl** key, select the block with the left mouse button, then drag it to a new location. You can also do this by dragging the block using the right mouse button. Duplicated blocks have the same parameter values as the original blocks. Sequence numbers are added to the new block names.

Deleting Blocks

To delete one or more blocks, select the blocks to be deleted and press the **Delete** or **Backspace** key. You can also choose **Clear** or **Cut** from the **Edit** menu. The **Cut** command writes the blocks into the clipboard, which enables you to paste them into a model. Using the **Delete** or **Backspace** key or the **Clear** command does not enable you to paste the block later.

You can use the **Undo** command from the **Edit** menu to replace a deleted block.

Setting Block Parameters

All Simulink blocks have a common set of parameters, called block properties, that you can set (see "Common Block Parameters" in the online Simulink Help). See "Block Properties Dialog Box" on page 6-8 for information on setting block properties. In addition, many blocks have one or more block-specific parameters that you can set (see "Block-Specific Parameters" in the online Simulink reference). By setting these parameters, you can customize the behavior of the block to meet the specific requirements of your model.

Setting Block-Specific Parameters

Every block that has block-specific parameters has a dialog box that you can use to view and set the parameters. You can display this dialog by selecting the block in the model window and choosing **BLOCK Parameters** from the model window's **Edit** menu or from the model window's context (right-click) menu, where **BLOCK** is the name of the block you selected, e.g., **Constant Parameters**. You can also display a block's parameter dialog box by double-clicking its icon in the model or library window.

Note This holds true for all blocks with parameter dialog boxes except for the Subsystem block. You must use the model window's **Edit** menu or context menu to display a Subsystem block's parameter dialog.

For information on the parameter dialog of a specific block, see the block's documentation in the "Simulink Blocks" in the online Simulink Help.

You can set any block parameter, using the Simulink `set_param` command. See `set_param` in the online Simulink Help for details.

You can use any MATLAB constant, variable, or expression that evaluates to an acceptable result when specifying the value of a parameter in a block parameter dialog or a `set_param` command.

Block Properties Dialog Box

This dialog box lets you set a block's properties. To display this dialog, select the block in the model window and then select **Block Properties** from the **Edit** menu.

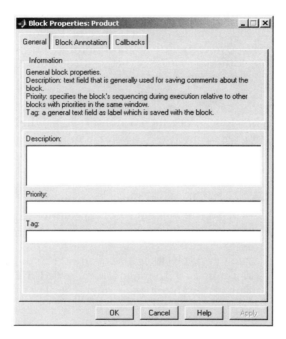

The dialog box contains the following tabbed panes.

General Pane

This pane allows you to set the following properties.

Description. Brief description of the block's purpose.

Priority. Execution priority of this block relative to other blocks in the model. See "Assigning Block Priorities" on page 6-16 for more information.

Tag. Text that is assigned to the block's Tag parameter and saved with the block in the model. You can the tag to create your own block-specific label for a block.

Block Annotation Pane

The block annotation pane allows you to display the values of selected parameters of a block in an annotation that appears beneath the block's icon.

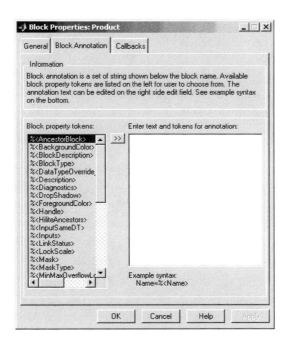

Enter the text of the annotation in the text field that appears on the right side of the pane. The text can include block property tokens, for example

```
%<Name>
Priority = %<priority>
```

of the form %<param> where param is the name of a parameter of the block. When displaying the annotation, Simulink replaces the tokens with the values of the corresponding parameters, e.g.,

Product
Priority = 2

The block property tag list on the left side of the pane lists all the tags that are valid for the currently selected block. To include one of the listed tags in the annotation, select the tag and then click the button between the tag list and the annotation field.

You can also create block annotations programmatically. See "Creating Block Annotations Programmatically" on page 6-11.

Callbacks Pane

The **Callbacks Pane** allows you to specify implementations for a block's callbacks (see "Using Callback Routines" on page 5-48).

To specify an implementation for a callback, select the callback in the callback list on the left side of the pane. Then enter MATLAB commands that implement the callback in the right-hand field. Click **OK** or **Append** to save the change. Simulink appends an asterisk to the name of the saved callback to indicate that it has been implemented.

Creating Block Annotations Programmatically

You can use a block's `AttributesFormatString` parameter to display selected parameters of a block beneath the block as an "attributes format string," i.e. a string that specifies values of the block's attributes (parameters). The "Model and Block Parameters" section in the online Simulink reference describes the parameters that a block can have. Use Simulink's `set_param` command to set this parameter to the desired attributes format string.

The attributes format string can be any text string that has embedded parameter names. An embedded parameter name is a parameter name preceded by `%<` and followed by `>`, for example, `%<priority>`. Simulink displays the attributes format string beneath the block's icon, replacing each parameter name with the corresponding parameter value. You can use line-feed characters (`\n`) to display each parameter on a separate line. For example, specifying the attributes format string

```
pri=%<priority>\ngain=%<Gain>
```

for a Gain block displays

If a parameter's value is not a string or an integer, Simulink displays `N/S` (not supported) for the parameter's value. If the parameter name is invalid, Simulink displays `???` as the parameter value.

State Properties Dialog Box

The **State Properties** dialog box allows you to specify code generation options for certain blocks with discrete states. To get help on using this dialog box, you must install the Real-Time Workshop documentation. See "Block States: Storing and Interfacing" in the online documentation for Real-Time Workshop for more information.

Changing a Block's Appearance

The Simulink Editor allows you to change the size, orientation, color, and label location of a block in a block diagram.

Changing the Orientation of a Block

By default, signals flow through a block from left to right. Input ports are on the left, and output ports are on the right. You can change the orientation of a block by choosing one of these commands from the **Format** menu:

- The **Flip Block** command rotates the block 180 degrees.
- The **Rotate Block** command rotates a block clockwise 90 degrees.

The figure below shows how Simulink orders ports after changing the orientation of a block using the **Rotate Block** and **Flip Block** menu items. The text in the blocks shows their orientation.

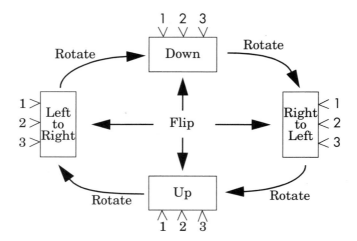

Resizing a Block's Icon

To change the size of a block, select it, then drag any of its selection handles. While you hold down the mouse button, a dotted rectangle shows the new block size. When you release the mouse button, the block is resized.

For example, the figure below shows a Signal Generator block being resized. The lower-right handle was selected and dragged to the cursor position. When the mouse button is released, the block takes its new size.

This figure shows a block being resized.

Displaying Parameters Beneath a Block's Icon

You can cause Simulink to display one or more of a block's parameters beneath the block's icon in a block diagram. You specify the parameters to be displayed in the following ways:

- By entering an attributes format string in the **Attributes format string** field of the block's **Block Properties** dialog box (see "Block Properties Dialog Box" on page 6-8)
- By setting the value of the block's AttributesFormatString property to the format string, using set_param

Using Drop Shadows

You can add a drop shadow to a block by selecting the block, then choosing **Show Drop Shadow** from the **Format** menu. When you select a block with a drop shadow, the menu item changes to **Hide Drop Shadow**. The figure below shows a Subsystem block with a drop shadow.

Manipulating Block Names

All block names in a model must be unique and must contain at least one character. By default, block names appear below blocks whose ports are on the sides, and to the left of blocks whose ports are on the top and bottom, as this figure shows.

Left to right

Top to bottom

Changing Block Names

You can edit a block name in one of these ways:

- To replace the block name, click the block name, double-click or drag the cursor to select the entire name, then enter the new name.
- To insert characters, click between two characters to position the insertion point, then insert text.
- To replace characters, drag the mouse to select a range of text to replace, then enter the new text.

When you click the pointer anywhere else in the model or take any other action, the name is accepted or rejected. If you try to change the name of a block to a name that already exists or to a name with no characters, Simulink displays an error message.

You can modify the font used in a block name by selecting the block, then choosing the **Font** menu item from the **Format** menu. Select a font from the **Set Font** dialog box. This procedure also changes the font of text on the block icon.

You can cancel edits to a block name by choosing **Undo** from the **Edit** menu.

Note If you change the name of a library block, all links to that block become unresolved.

Changing the Location of a Block Name

You can change the location of the name of a selected block in two ways:

- By dragging the block name to the opposite side of the block.
- By choosing the **Flip Name** command from the **Format** menu. This command changes the location of the block name to the opposite side of the block.

For more information about block orientation, see "Changing the Orientation of a Block" on page 6-12.

Changing Whether a Block Name Appears

To change whether the name of a selected block is displayed, choose a menu item from the **Format** menu:

- The **Hide Name** menu item hides a visible block name. When you select **Hide Name**, it changes to **Show Name** when that block is selected.

- The **Show Name** menu item shows a hidden block name.

Specifying a Block's Color

See "Specifying Block Diagram Colors" on page 5-5 for information on how to set the color of a block.

Controlling and Displaying Block Execution Order

The Simulink Editor allows you to control and display the order in which Simulink executes blocks.

Assigning Block Priorities

You can assign execution priorities to nonvirtual blocks or virtual subsystem blocks in a model (see "Virtual Blocks" on page 6-2). Higher priority blocks execute before lower priority blocks, though not necessarily before blocks that have no assigned priority.

You can assign block priorities interactively or programmatically. To set priorities programmatically, use the command

```
set_param(b,'Priority','n')
```

where b is a block path and n is any valid integer. (Negative numbers and 0 are valid priority values.) The lower the number, the higher the priority; that is, 2 is higher priority than 3. To set a block's priority interactively, enter the priority in the **Priority** field of the block's **Block Properties** dialog box (see "Block Properties Dialog Box" on page 6-8).

Simulink honors the block priorities that you specify only if they are consistent with the Simulink block sorting algorithm (see "Determining Block Update Order" on page 3-10). If the specified priorities are inconsistent, Simulink ignores the specified priority and places the block in an appropriate location in the block execution order. If Simulink is unable to honor a block priority, it displays a Block Priority Violation diagnostic message (see "The Diagnostics Pane" on page 8-24).

Displaying Block Execution Order

To display the execution order of blocks during simulation, select **Execution order** from the Simulink **Format** menu. Selecting this option causes Simulink to display a number in the top right corner of each block in a block diagram.

The number indicates the execution order of the block relative to other blocks in the diagram. For example, 1 indicates that the block is the first block executed on every time step, 2 indicates that the block is the second block executed on every time step, and so on.

Look-Up Table Editor

The Look-Up Table Editor allows you to inspect and change the table elements of any look-up table (LUT) block in a model (see "Look-Up Tables" in the online Simulink documentation), including custom LUT blocks that you have created, using the Simulink Mask Editor (see "Editing Custom LUT Blocks" on page 6-23). You can also use a block's parameter dialog to edit its table. However, that requires you to open the subsystem containing the block first and than its parameter dialog box first The LUT editor allows you to skip these steps. This section explains how to open and use the LUT editor to edit LUT blocks.

Note You cannot use the LUT Editor to change the dimensions of a look-up table. You must use the block's parameter dialog box for this purpose.

To open the editor, select **Look-up table editor** from the Simulink **Tools** menu. The editor appears.

The editor contains two panes. The pane on the left is a LUT block browser. It allows you to browse and select LUT blocks in any open model (see "Browsing LUT Blocks" on page 6-19). The pane on the right allows you to edit the selected block's look-up table ("Editing Table Values" on page 6-20).

Browsing LUT Blocks

The **Models** list in the upper left corner of the LUT Editor lists the names of all models open in the current MATLAB session.To browse any open model's LUT table blocks, select the model's name from the list. A tree-structured view of the selected model's LUT blocks appears in the **Table blocks** field beneath the **Models** list.

The tree view initially lists all the LUT blocks that reside at the model's root level. It also displays any subsystems that contain LUT blocks. Clicking the expand button (+) to the left of the subsystem's name expands the tree to show the LUT blocks in that subsystem. The expanded view also shows any subsystems in the expanded subsystem. You can continue expanding subsystem nodes in this manner to display LUT blocks at any level in the model hierarchy.

Clicking any LUT block in the LUT block tree view displays the block's look-up table in the right hand pane, allowing you to edit the table (see"Editing Table Values" on page 6-20).

Note If you want to browse the LUT blocks in a model that is not currently open, you can command the LUT Editor to open the model. To do this, select **Open** from the LUT Editor's **File** menu.

Editing Table Values

The **Block parameters data** table view of the LUT Editor allows you to edit the look-up table of the LUT block currently selected in the adjacent tree view.

The table view displays the entire table if it is one- or two-dimensional or a two-dimensional slice of the table if the table has more than two dimensions (see "Displaying N-D Tables" on page 6-21). To change any of the displayed values, double-click the value. The LUT Editor replaces the value with an edit field containing the value. Edit the value, then press **Return** or click outside the field to confirm the change.

The LUT Editor records your changes in a copy of the table that it maintains. To update the copy maintained by the LUT block itself, select **Update block data** from the LUT Editor's **File** menu. To restore the LUT Editor 's copy to the values stored in the block, select **Reload block data** from the **File** menu.

Displaying N-D Tables

If the look-up table of the LUT block currently selected in the LUT Editor's tree view has more than two dimensions, the editor's table view displays a two-dimensional slice of the table.

Block Parameters Data:				
(1)	(2)	(3)	(4)	
2401	2421	2441	2461	▲
2402	2422	2442	2462	
2403	2423	2443	2463	
2404	2424	2444	2464	
2405	2425	2445	2465	
2406	2426	2446	2466	
2407	2427	2447	2467	
2408	2428	2448	2468	
2409	2429	2449	2469	▼

n-D Data Dimension Selector: viewing table data: (:,:,1,7)				
Dimension size	20	4	5	7
Select 2-D slice	: ▾	: ▾	1 ▾	7 ▾
Select row axis	⦿	○	○	○
Select column axis	○	⦿	○	○

The **n-D Data Dimension Selector** beneath the table specifies which slice currently appears and allows you to select another slice. The selector consists of a 4-by-N array of controls where N is the number of dimensions in the look-up table. Each column corresponds to a dimension of the look-up table. The first column corresponds to the first dimension of the table, the second column to the second dimension of the table, and so on. The top row of the selector array displays the size of each dimension. The remaining rows specify which dimensions of the table correspond to the row and column axes of the slice and the indices that select the slice from the remaining dimensions.

To select another slice of the table, click the **Select row axis** and **Select column axis** radio buttons in the columns that correspond to the dimensions that you want to view. Then select the indexes of the slice from the pop-up index lists in the remaining columns.

For example, the following selector displays slice (:,: ,1,7) of a 4-D table.

n-D Data Dimension Selector: viewing table data: (:,:,1,7)				
Dimension size	20	4	5	7
Select 2-D slice	: ▾	: ▾	1 ▾	7 ▾
Select row axis	⦿	○	○	○
Select column axis	○	⦿	○	○

Plotting LUT Tables

Select **Linear** or **Mesh** from the **Plot** menu of the LUT Editor to display a
linear or mesh plot of the table or table slice currently displayed in the editor's
table view.

Editing Custom LUT Blocks

You can use the LUT Editor to edit custom look-up table blocks that you or others have created. To do this, you must first configure the LUT Editor to recognize the custom LUT blocks in your model. Once you have configured the LUT Editor to recognize the custom blocks, you can edit them as if they were standard blocks.

To configure the LUT editor to recognize custom LUT blocks, select **Configure** from the editor's **File** menu. The **Look-Up Table Blocks Type Configuration** dialog box appears.

By default the dialog box displays a table of the types of LUT blocks that the LUT Editor currently recognizes. By default these are the standard Simulink LUT blocks. Each row of the table displays key attributes of a LUT block type.

Adding a Custom LUT Type

To add a custom block to the list of recognized types,

1 Select the **Add** button on the dialog box.

A new row appears at the bottom of the block type table.

2 Enter information for the custom block in the new row under the following headings.

Field Name	Description
Block Type	Block type of the custom LUT block. The block type is the value of the block's BlockType parameter.
Mask Type	Mask type in this field. The mask type is the value of the block's MaskType parameter.
Breakpoint Name	Names of the custom LUT block's parameters that store its breakpoints.
Table Name	Name of the block parameter that stores the custom block's look-up table.
Number of dimensions	Leave empty.
Explicit Dimensions	Leave empty.

3 Select **OK**.

Removing Custom LUT Types

To remove a custom LUT type from the list of types recognized by the LUT Editor, select the custom type's entry in the table in the **Look-Up Table Blocks Type Configuration** dialog box. Then select **Remove**. To remove all custom LUT types, check the check box labeled **Use Simulink default look-up table blocks list** at the top of the dialog box.

Working with Block Libraries

Libraries enable users to copy blocks into their models from external libraries and automatically update the copied blocks when the source blocks change. Using libraries allows users who develop their own block libraries, or who use those provided by others (such as blocksets), to ensure that their models automatically include the most recent versions of these blocks.

Terminology

It is important to understand the terminology used with this feature.

Library – A collection of library blocks. A library must be explicitly created using **New Library** from the **File** menu.

Library block – A block in a library.

Reference block – A copy of a library block.

Link – The connection between the reference block and its library block that allows Simulink to update the reference block when the library block changes.

Copy – The operation that creates a reference block from either a library block or another reference block.

This figure illustrates this terminology.

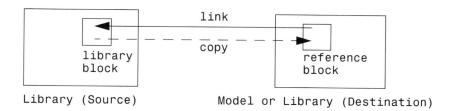

Library (Source)   Model or Library (Destination)

Simulink Block Library

Simulink comes with a library of standard blocks called the Simulink block library. See "Starting Simulink" on page 4-2 for information on displaying and using this library.

Creating a Library Link

To create a link to a library block in a model, copy the block's icon from the library to the model (see "Copying and Moving Blocks from One Window to Another" on page 6-4) or by dragging the block from the Library Browser (see "Browsing Block Libraries" on page 6-31) into the model window.

When you copy a library block into a model or another library, Simulink creates a link to the library block. The reference block is a copy of the library block. You can change the values of the reference block's parameters but you cannot mask the block or, if it is masked, edit the mask. Also, you cannot set callback parameters for a reference block. If the link is to a subsystem, you can modify the contents of the reference subsystem (see "Modifying a Linked Subsystem" on page 6-27).

The library and reference blocks are linked *by name*; that is, the reference block is linked to the specific block and library whose names are in effect at the time the copy is made.

If Simulink is unable to find either the library block or the source library on your MATLAB path when it attempts to update the reference block, the link becomes *unresolved*. Simulink issues an error message and displays these blocks using red dashed lines. The error message is

```
Failed to find block "source-block-name"
in library "source-library-name"
referenced by block
"reference-block-path".
```

The unresolved reference block is displayed like this (colored red).

To fix a bad link, you must do one of the following:

- Delete the unlinked reference block and copy the library block back into your model.
- Add the directory that contains the required library to the MATLAB path and select **Update Diagram** from the **Edit** menu.

- Double-click the reference block. On the dialog box that appears, correct the pathname and click **Apply** or **Close**.

Disabling Library Links

Simulink allows you to disable linked blocks in a model. Simulink ignores disabled links when simulating a model. To disable a link, select the link, choose **Link options** from the model window's **Edit** or context menu, then choose **Disable link**. To restore a disabled link, choose **Restore link** from the **Link Options** menu.

Modifying a Linked Subsystem

Simulink allows you to modify subsystems that are library links. If your modifications alter the structure of the subsystem, you must disable the link from the reference block to the library block. If you attempt to modify the structure of a subsystem link, Simulink prompts you to disable the link. Examples of structural modifications include adding or deleting a block or line or changing the number of ports on a block. Examples of nonstructural changes include changes to parameter values that do not affect the structure of the subsystem.

Propagating Link Modifications

Simulink allows a model to have active links with nonstructural but not structural changes. If you restore a link that has structural changes, Simulink prompts you to either propagate or discard the changes. If you choose to propagate the changes, Simulink updates the library block with the changes made in the reference block. If you choose to discard the changes, Simulink replaces the modified reference block with the original library block. In either case, the end result is that the reference block is an exact copy of the library block.

If you restore a link with nonstructural changes, Simulink enables the link without prompting you to propagate or discard the changes. If you want to propagate or discard the changes at a later time, select the reference block, choose **Link options** from the model window's **Edit** or context menu, then choose **Propagate/Discard changes**. If you want to view the nonstructural parameter differences between a reference block and its corresponding library block, choose **View changes** from the **Link options** menu.

Updating a Linked Block

Simulink updates out-of-date reference blocks in a model or library at these times:

- When the model or library is loaded
- When you select **Update Diagram** from the **Edit** menu or run the simulation
- When you query the LinkStatus parameter of a block, using the get_param command (see "Library Link Status" on page 6-29)
- When you use the find_system command

Breaking a Link to a Library Block

You can break the link between a reference block and its library block to cause the reference block to become a simple copy of the library block, unlinked to the library block. Changes to the library block no longer affect the block. Breaking links to library blocks may enable you to transport a model as a stand-alone model, without the libraries.

To break the link between a reference block and its library block, first disable the block. Then select the block and choose **Break Library Link** from the **Link options** menu. You can also break the link between a reference block and its library block from the command line by changing the value of the LinkStatus parameter to 'none' using this command:

```
set_param('refblock', 'LinkStatus', 'none')
```

You can save a system and break all links between reference blocks and library blocks using this command:

```
save_system('sys', 'newname', 'BreakLinks')
```

Note Breaking library links in a model does not guarantee that you can run the model stand-alone, especially if the model includes blocks from third-party libraries or optional Simulink blocksets. It is possible that a library block invokes functions supplied with the library and hence can run only if the library is installed on the system running the model. Further, breaking a link can cause a model to fail when you install a new version of the library on a system. For example, suppose a block invokes a function that is supplied with the library. Now suppose that a new version of the library eliminates the function. Running a model with an unlinked copy of the block results in invocation of a now nonexistent function, causing the simulation to fail. To avoid such problems, you should generally avoid breaking links to third-party libraries and optional Simulink blocksets.

Finding the Library Block for a Reference Block

To find the source library and block linked to a reference block, select the reference block, then choose **Go To Library Link** from the **Link options** submenu of the model window's **Edit** or context menu. If the library is open, Simulink selects and highlights the library block and makes the source library the active window. If the library is not open, Simulink opens it and selects the library block.

Library Link Status

All blocks have a LinkStatus parameter that indicates whether the block is a reference block. The parameter can have these values.

Status	Description
none	Block is not a reference block.
resolved	Link is resolved.
unresolved	Link is unresolved.
implicit	Block is within a linked block.
inactive	Link is disabled.

Displaying Library Links

Simulink optionally displays an arrow in the bottom left corner of each icon that represents a library link in a model.

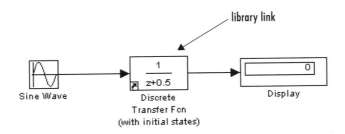

This arrow allows you to tell at a glance whether an icon represents a link to a library block or a local instance of a block. To enable display of library links, select **Library Link Display** from the model window's **Format** menu and then select either **User** (displays only links to user libraries) or **All** (displays all links).

The color of the link arrow indicates the status of the link.

Color	Status
Black	Active link
Grey	Inactive link
Red	Active and modified

Getting Information About Library Blocks

Use the libinfo command to get information about reference blocks in a system. The format for the command is

```
libdata = libinfo(sys)
```

where sys is the name of the system. The command returns a structure of size n-by-1, where n is the number of library blocks in sys. Each element of the structure has four fields:

- Block, the block path
- Library, the library name
- ReferenceBlock, the reference block path
- LinkStatus, the link status, either 'resolved' or 'unresolved'

Browsing Block Libraries

The Library Browser lets you quickly locate and copy library blocks into a model. To display the Library Browser, click the **Library Browser** button in the toolbar of the MATLAB desktop or Simulink model window or enter simulink at the MATLAB command line.

Note The Library Browser is available only on Microsoft Windows platforms.

The Library Browser contains three panes.

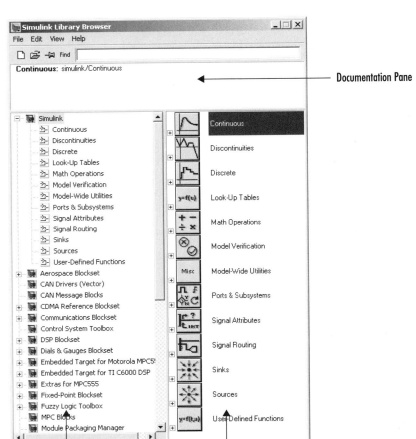

Documentation Pane

Tree Pane   Icon Pane

The tree pane displays all the block libraries installed on your system. The icon pane displays the icons of the blocks that reside in the library currently selected in the tree pane. The documentation pane displays documentation for the block selected in the icon pane.

You can locate blocks either by navigating the Library Browser's library tree or by using the Library Browser's search facility.

Navigating the Library Tree

The library tree displays a list of all the block libraries installed on the system. You can view or hide the contents of libraries by expanding or collapsing the tree using the mouse or keyboard. To expand/collapse the tree, click the +/- buttons next to library entries or select an entry and press the +/- or right/left arrow key on your keyboard. Use the up/down arrow keys to move up or down the tree.

Searching Libraries

To find a particular block, enter the block's name in the edit field next to the Library Browser's **Find** button, then click the **Find** button.

Opening a Library

To open a library, right-click the library's entry in the browser. Simulink displays an **Open Library** button. Select the **Open Library** button to open the library.

Creating and Opening Models

To create a model, select the **New** button on the Library Browser's toolbar. To open an existing model, select the **Open** button on the toolbar.

Copying Blocks

To copy a block from the Library Browser into a model, select the block in the browser, drag the selected block into the model window, and drop it where you want to create the copy.

Displaying Help on a Block

To display help on a block, right-click the block in the Library Browser and select the button that subsequently pops up.

Pinning the Library Browser

To keep the Library Browser above all other windows on your desktop, select the **PushPin** button on the browser's toolbar.

Adding Libraries to the Library Browser

If you want a library that you have created to appear in the Library Browser, you must create an slblocks.m file that describes the library in the directory that contains it. The easiest way to create an `slblocks.m` file is to use an existing `slblocks.m` file as a template. You can find all existing `slblocks.m` files on your system by typing

```
which('slblocks.m', '-all')
```

at the MATLAB command prompt. Copy any of the displayed files to your library's directory. Then open the copy, edit it, following the instructions included in the file, and save the result. Finally, add your library's directory to the MATLAB path, if necessary. The next time you open the Library Browser, your library should appear among the libraries displayed in the browser.

Working with Signals

This section describes how to create and use Simulink signals.

Signal Basics

This section provides an overview of Simulink signals and explains how to specify, display, and check the validity of signal connections.

About Signals

Signals are the streams of values that appear at the outputs of Simulink blocks when a model is simulated. It is useful to think of signals as traveling along the lines that connect the blocks in a model diagram. But note that the lines in a Simulink model represent logical, not physical, connections among blocks. Thus, the analogy between Simulink signals and electrical signals is not complete. Electrical signals, for example, take time to cross a wire. The output of a Simulink block, by contrast, appears instantaneously at the input of the block to which it is connected.

Signal Dimensions

Simulink blocks can output one- or two-dimensional signals. A one-dimensional (1-D) signal consists of a stream of one-dimensional arrays output at a frequency of one array (vector) per simulation time step. A two-dimensional (2-D) signal consists of a stream of two-dimensional arrays emitted at a frequency of one 2-D array (matrix) per block sample time. The Simulink user interface and documentation generally refer to 1-D signals as *vectors* and 2-D signals as *matrices*. A one-element array is frequently referred to as a *scalar*. A *row vector* is a 2-D array that has one row. A *column vector* is a 2-D array that has one column.

Simulink blocks vary in the dimensionality of the signals they can accept or output during simulation. Some blocks can accept or output signals of any dimensions. Some can accept or output only scalar or vector signals. To determine the signal dimensionality of a particular block, see the block's description in "Simulink Blocks" in the online Simulink Help. See "Determining Output Signal Dimensions" on page 7-6 for information on what determines the dimensions of output signals for blocks that can output nonscalar signals.

Complex Signals

The values of Simulink signals can be complex numbers. A signal whose values are complex numbers is called a complex signal. See "Working with Complex

Signals" on page 7-11 for information on creating and manipulating complex signals.

Virtual Signals

A *virtual signal* is a signal that represents another signal graphically. Virtual blocks, such as a Bus Creator or Subsystem block (see "Virtual Blocks" on page 6-2), generate virtual signals. Like virtual blocks, virtual signals allow you to simplify your model graphically. For example, using a Bus Creator block, you can reduce a large number of nonvirtual signals (i.e., signals originating from nonvirtual blocks) to a single virtual signal, thereby making your model easier to understand. You can think of a virtual signal as a tie wrap that bundles together a number of signals.

Virtual signals are purely graphical entities. They have no mathematical or physical significance. Simulink ignores them when simulating a model.

Whenever you run or update a model, Simulink determines the nonvirtual signal(s) represented by the model's virtual signal(s), using a procedure known as *signal propagation*. When running the model, Simulink uses the corresponding nonvirtual signal(s), determined via signal propagation, to drive the blocks to which the virtual signals are connected. Consider, for example, the following model.

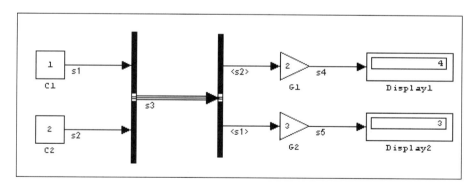

The signals driving Gain blocks G1 and G2 are virtual signals corresponding to signals s2 and s1, respectively. Simulink determines this automatically whenever you update or simulate the model.

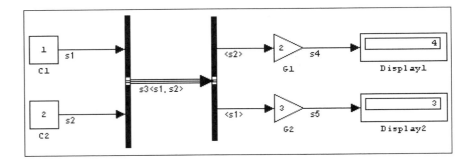

Note Virtual signals can represent virtual as well as nonvirtual signals. For example, you can use a Bus Creator block to combine multiple virtual and nonvirtual signals into a single virtual signal. If during signal propagation Simulink determines that a component of a virtual signal is itself virtual, Simulink determines its nonvirtual components using signal propagation. This process continues until Simulink has determined all nonvirtual components of a virtual signal.

Control Signals

A *control signal* is a signal used by one block to initiate execution of another block, e.g., a function-call or action subsystem. When you update or start simulation of a block diagram, Simulink uses a dash-dot pattern to redraw lines representing the diagram's control signals as illustrated in the following example.

Signal Buses

You can use Bus Creator and Bus Selector blocks to create signal buses.

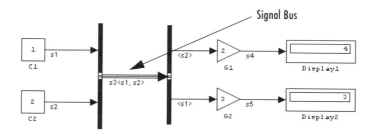

A signal bus is a virtual signal that represents a set of signals. It is analogous to a bundle of wires held together by tie wraps. Simulink uses a special line style to display signal buses. If you select **Signal Dimensions** from the **Format** menu, Simulink displays the number of signal components carried by the bus.

Signal Glossary

The following table summarizes the terminology used to describe signals in the Simulink user interface and documentation.

Term	Meaning
Complex signal	Signal whose values are complex numbers.
Data type	Format used to represent signal values internally.
Matrix	Two-dimensional signal array.
Real signal	Signal whose values are real (as opposed to complex) numbers.
Scalar	One-element array, i.e., a one-element, 1-D or 2-D array.
Signal bus	Signal created by a Mux or Demux block.

Term	Meaning
Signal propagation	Process used by Simulink to determine attributes of signals and blocks, such as data types, labels, sample time, dimensionality, and so on, that are determined by connectivity.
Size	Number of elements that a signal contains. The size of a matrix (2-D) signal is generally expressed as M-by-N where M is the number of columns and N is the number of rows making up the signal.
Vector	One-dimensional signal array.
Virtual signal	Signal that represents another signal or set of signals.
Width	Size of a vector signal.

Determining Output Signal Dimensions

If a block can emit nonscalar signals, the dimensions of the signals that the block outputs depend on the block's parameters, if the block is a source block; otherwise, the output dimensions depend on the dimensions of the block's input and parameters.

Determining the Output Dimensions of Source Blocks

A *source* block is a block that has no inputs. Examples of source blocks include the Constant block and the Sine Wave block. See the "Sources Library" table in the online Simulink Help for a complete listing of Simulink source blocks. The output dimensions of a source block are the same as those of its output value parameters if the block's **Interpret Vector Parameters as 1-D** parameter is off (i.e., not selected in the block's parameter dialog box). If the **Interpret Vector Parameters as 1-D** parameter is on, the output dimensions equal the output value parameter dimensions unless the parameter dimensions are N-by-1 or 1-by-N. In the latter case, the block outputs a vector signal of width N.

As an example of how a source block's output value parameter(s) and **Interpret Vector Parameters as 1-D** parameter determine the dimensionality of its output, consider the Constant block. This block outputs a constant signal equal to its **Constant value** parameter. The following table illustrates how the dimensionality of the **Constant value** parameter and the setting of the **Interpret Vector Parameters as 1-D** parameter determine the dimensionality of the block's output.

Constant Value	Interpret Vector Parameters as 1-D	Output
2-D scalar	off	2-D scalar
2-D scalar	on	1-D scalar
1-by-N matrix	off	1-by-N matrix
1-by-N matrix	on	N-element vector
N-by-1 matrix	off	N-by-1 matrix
N-by-1 matrix	on	N-element vector
M-by-N matrix	off	M-by-N matrix
M-by-N matrix	on	M-by-N matrix

Simulink source blocks allow you to specify the dimensions of the signals that they output. You can therefore use them to introduce signals of various dimensions into your model.

Determining the Output Dimensions of Nonsource Blocks

If a block has inputs, the dimensions of its outputs are, after scalar expansion, the same as those of its inputs. (All inputs must have the same dimensions, as discussed in the next section.)

Signal and Parameter Dimension Rules

When creating a Simulink model, you must observe the following rules regarding signal and parameter dimensions.

Input Signal Dimension Rule

All nonscalar inputs to a block must have the same dimensions.

A block can have a mix of scalar and nonscalar inputs as long as all the nonscalar inputs have the same dimensions. Simulink expands the scalar inputs to have the same dimensions as the nonscalar inputs (see "Scalar Expansion of Inputs" on page 7-9), thus preserving the general rule.

Block Parameter Dimension Rule

In general, a block's parameters must have the same dimensions as the corresponding inputs.

Two seeming exceptions exist to this general rule:

- A block can have scalar parameters corresponding to nonscalar inputs. In this case, Simulink expands a scalar parameter to have the same dimensions as the corresponding input (see "Scalar Expansion of Parameters" on page 7-9), thus preserving the general rule.
- If an input is a vector, the corresponding parameter can be either an N-by-1 or a 1-by-N matrix. In this case, Simulink applies the N matrix elements to the corresponding elements of the input vector. This exception allows use of MATLAB row or column vectors, which are actually 1-by-N or N-by-1 matrices, respectively, to specify parameters that apply to vector inputs.

Vector or Matrix Input Conversion Rules

Simulink converts vectors to row or column matrices and row or column matrices to vectors under the following circumstances:

- If a vector signal is connected to an input that requires a matrix, Simulink converts the vector to a one-row or one-column matrix.
- If a one-column or one-row matrix is connected to an input that requires a vector, Simulink converts the matrix to a vector.
- If the inputs to a block consist of a mixture of vectors and matrices and the matrix inputs all have one column or one row, Simulink converts the vectors to matrices having one column or one row, respectively.

Note You can configure Simulink to display a warning or error message if a vector or matrix conversion occurs during a simulation. See "Configuration options" on page 8-25 for more information.

Scalar Expansion of Inputs and Parameters

Scalar expansion is the conversion of a scalar value into a nonscalar array of the same dimensions. Many Simulink blocks support scalar expansion of inputs and parameters. Block descriptions in the "Simulink Blocks" section in the online Simulink Help indicate whether Simulink applies scalar expansion to a block's inputs and parameters.

Scalar Expansion of Inputs

Scalar expansion of inputs refers to the expansion of scalar inputs to match the dimensions of other nonscalar inputs or nonscalar parameters. When the input to a block is a mix of scalar and nonscalar signals, Simulink expands the scalar inputs into nonscalar signals having the same dimensions as the other nonscalar inputs. The elements of an expanded signal equal the value of the scalar from which the signal was expanded.

The following model illustrates scalar expansion of inputs. This model adds scalar and vector inputs. The input from block Constant1 is scalar expanded to match the size of the vector input from the Constant block. The input is expanded to the vector [3 3 3].

When a block's output is a function of a parameter and the parameter is nonscalar, Simulink expands a scalar input to match the dimensions of the parameter. For example, Simulink expands a scalar input to a Gain block to match the dimensions of a nonscalar gain parameter.

Scalar Expansion of Parameters

If a block has a nonscalar input and a corresponding parameter is a scalar, Simulink expands the scalar parameter to have the same number of elements as the input. Each element of the expanded parameter equals the value of the original scalar. Simulink then applies each element of the expanded parameter to the corresponding input element.

This example shows that a scalar parameter (the Gain) is expanded to a vector of identically valued elements to match the size of the block input, a three-element vector.

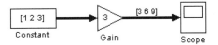

Working with Complex Signals

By default, the values of Simulink signals are real numbers. However, models can create and manipulate signals that have complex numbers as values.

You can introduce a complex-valued signal into a model in the following ways:

- Load complex-valued signal data from the MATLAB workspace into the model via a root-level inport.
- Create a Constant block in your model and set its value to a complex number.
- Create real signals corresponding to the real and imaginary parts of a complex signal, then combine the parts into a complex signal, using the Real-Imag to Complex conversion block.

You can manipulate complex signals via blocks that accept them. If you are not sure whether a block accepts complex signals, see the documentation for the block in the "Simulink blocks" section of the Simulink online documentation.

Checking Signal Connections

Many Simulink blocks have limitations on the types of signals they can accept. Before simulating a model, Simulink checks all blocks to ensure that they can accommodate the types of signals output by the ports to which they are connected. If any incompatibilities exist, Simulink reports an error and terminates the simulation. To detect such errors before running a simulation, choose **Update Diagram** from the Simulink **Edit** menu. Simulink reports any invalid connections found in the process of updating the diagram.

Displaying Signals

A model window's **Format** menu and its model context (right-click) menu offer the following options for displaying signal attributes.

Wide nonscalar lines

Draws lines that carry vector or matrix signals wider than lines that carry scalar signals.

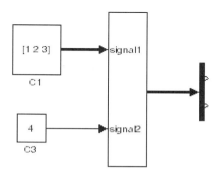

Signal dimensions

Display the dimensions of nonscalar signals next to the line that carries the signal.

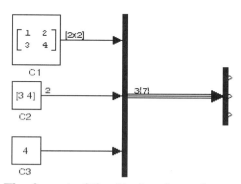

The format of the display depends on whether the line represents a single signal or a bus. If the line represents a single vector signal, Simulink displays the width of the signal. If the line represents a single matrix signal, Simulink displays its dimensions as $[N_1 \times N_2]$ where N_i is the size of the ith dimension of the signal. If the line represents a bus carrying signals of the same data type, Simulink displays $N\{M\}$ where N is the number of signals carried by the bus and M is the total number of signal elements carried by the bus. If the bus carries signals of different data types, Simulink displays only the total number of signal elements $\{M\}$.

Port data types

Displays the data type of a signal next to the output port that emits the signal.

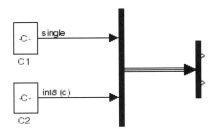

The notation (c) following the data type of a signal indicates that the signal is complex.

Signal Names

You can assign names to signals by

- Editing the signal's label
- Setting the name parameter of the port or line that represents the signal, e.g.,

```
p = get_param(gcb, 'PortHandles')
l = get_param(p.Inport, 'Line')
set_param(l, 'Name', 's9')
```

Signal Labels

A signal's label displays the signal's name. A virtual signal's label optionally displays the signals it represents in angle brackets. You can edit a signal's label, thereby changing the signal's name.

To create a signal label (and thereby name the signal), double-click the line that represents the signal. The text cursor appears. Enter the name and click anywhere outside the label to exit label editing mode.

Note When you create a signal label, take care to double-click the line. If you click in an unoccupied area close to the line, you will create a model annotation instead.

Labels can appear above or below horizontal lines or line segments, and left or right of vertical lines or line segments. Labels can appear at either end, at the center, or in any combination of these locations.

To move a signal label, drag the label to a new location on the line. When you release the mouse button, the label fixes its position near the line.

To copy a signal label, hold down the **Ctrl** key while dragging the label to another location on the line. When you release the mouse button, the label appears in both the original and the new locations.

To edit an existing signal label, select it:

- To replace the label, click the label, double-click or drag the cursor to select the entire label, then enter the new label.
- To insert characters, click between two characters to position the insertion point, then insert text.
- To replace characters, drag the mouse to select a range of text to replace, then enter the new text.

To delete all occurrences of a signal label, delete all the characters in the label. When you click outside the label, the labels are deleted. To delete a single occurrence of the label, hold down the **Shift** key while you select the label, then press the **Delete** or **Backspace** key.

To change the font of a signal label, select the signal, choose **Font** from the **Format** menu, then select a font from the **Set Font** dialog box.

Displaying Signals Represented by Virtual Signals

To display the signal(s) represented by a virtual signal, click the signal's label and enter an angle bracket (<) after the signal's name. (If the signal has no name, simply enter the angle bracket.) Click anywhere outside the signal's label. Simulink exits label editing mode and displays the signals represented by the virtual signal in brackets in the label.

Running a Simulation

The following sections explain how to run a Simulink simulation.

Simulation Basics

Running a Simulink model is generally a two-step process. First, you specify various simulation parameters, such as the solver used to solve the model, the start and stop time for the simulation, the maximum step size, and so on (see "Specifying Simulation Parameters" on page 8-2). You then start the simulation. Simulink runs the simulation from the specified start time to the specified stop time (see "Starting a Simulation" on page 8-3). While the simulation is running, you can interact with the simulation in various ways, stop or pause the simulation (see "Pausing or Stopping a Simulation" on page 8-5), and launch simulations of other models. If an error occurs during a simulation, Simulink halts the simulation and pops up a diagnostic viewer that helps you to determine the cause of the error.

Specifying Simulation Parameters

To use the **Simulation Parameters** dialog box:

1 Open or select the model whose simulation parameters you want to set.

2 Select **Simulation parameters** from the model window's **Simulation** menu.

The **Simulation Parameters** dialog box appears.

The dialog box displays the current simulation settings for the model (see "The Simulation Parameters Dialog Box" on page 8-7 for a detailed description of the settings).

3 Change the settings as necessary to suit your needs.

   You can specify parameters as valid MATLAB expressions, consisting of constants, workspace variable names, MATLAB functions, and mathematical operators.

4 Click **Apply** to confirm the changes or **OK** to confirm the changes and dismiss the dialog box.

5 If desired, save the model to save the changes to the model's simulation parameters.

Controlling Execution of a Simulation

The Simulink graphical interface includes menu commands and toolbar buttons that enable you to start, stop, and pause a simulation.

Starting a Simulation

To start execution of a model, select **Start** from the model editor's **Simulation** menu or click the **Start** button on the model's toolbar.

You can also use the keyboard shortcut, **Ctrl+T**, to start the simulation.

Note A common mistake that new Simulink users make is to start a simulation while the Simulink block library is the active window. Make sure your model window is the active window before starting a simulation.

Simulink starts executing the model at the start time specified on the **Simulation Parameters** dialog box. Execution continues until the simulation reaches the final time step specified on the **Simulation Parameters** dialog box, an error occurs, or you pause or terminate the simulation (see "The Simulation Parameters Dialog Box" on page 8-7).

While the simulation is running, a progress bar at the bottom of the model window shows how far the simulation has progressed. A **Stop** command replaces the **Start** command on the **Simulation** menu. A **Pause** command appears on the menu and replaces the **Start** button on the model toolbar.

Your computer beeps to signal the completion of the simulation.

Pausing or Stopping a Simulation

Select the **Pause** command or button to pause the simulation. Simulink completes execution of the current time step and suspends execution of the simulation. When you select **Pause**, the menu item and button change to **Continue**. (The button has the same appearance as the **Start** button). You can resume a suspended simulation at the next time step by choosing **Continue**.

To terminate execution of the model, select the **Stop** command or button. The keyboard shortcut for stopping a simulation is **Ctrl+T**, the same as for starting a simulation. Simulink completes execution of the current time step before terminating the model. Subsequently selecting the **Start** command or button restarts the simulation at the first time step specified on the **Simulation Parameters** dialog box.

If the model includes any blocks that write output to a file or to the workspace, or if you select output options on the **Simulation Parameters** dialog box, Simulink writes the data when the simulation is terminated or suspended.

Interacting with a Running Simulation

You can perform certain operations interactively while a simulation is running. You can

- Modify many simulation parameters, including the stop time, the solver, and the maximum step size
- Change the solver
- Click a line to see the signal carried on that line on a floating (unconnected) Scope or Display block
- Modify the parameters of a block, as long as you do not cause a change in
  - Number of states, inputs, or outputs
  - Sample time
  - Number of zero crossings
  - Vector length of any block parameters
  - Length of the internal block work vectors

You cannot make changes to the structure of the model, such as adding or deleting lines or blocks, during a simulation. If you need to make these kinds of changes, you need to stop the simulation, make the change, then start the simulation again to see the results of the change.

The Simulation Parameters Dialog Box

This section discusses the simulation parameters, which you specify either on the **Simulation Parameters** dialog box or using `sim` and `simset` commands. Parameters are described as they appear on the dialog box panes.

The Solver Pane

The **Solver** pane appears when you first choose **Parameters** from the **Simulation** menu or when you select the **Solver** tab.

The **Solver** pane allows you to

- Set the simulation start and stop times
- Choose the solver and specify its parameters
- Select output options

Simulation Time

You can change the start time and stop time for the simulation by entering new values in the **Start time** and **Stop time** fields. The default start time is 0.0 seconds and the default stop time is 10.0 seconds.

Simulation time and actual clock time are not the same. For example, running a simulation for 10 seconds usually does not take 10 seconds. The amount of time it takes to run a simulation depends on many factors, including the model's complexity, the solver's step sizes, and the computer's speed.

Solvers

Simulation of a Simulink model entails computing its inputs, outputs, and states at intervals from the simulation start time to the simulation end time. Simulink uses a solver to perform this task. No one method for solving a model is suitable for all models. Simulink therefore provides an assortment of solvers, each geared to solving a specific type of model. The **Solver** pane allows you to select the solver most suitable for your model (see "Improving Simulation Performance and Accuracy" on page 8-39 for information on choosing a solver). Your choices include

- Fixed-step continuous solvers
- Variable-step continuous solvers
- Fixed-step discrete solver
- Variable-step discrete solver

Fixed-step continuous solvers. These solvers compute a model's continuous states at equally spaced time steps from the simulation start time to the simulation stop time. The solvers use numerical integration to compute the continuous states of a system from the state derivatives specified by the model. Each solver uses a different integration method, allowing you to choose the method most suitable for your model. To specify a fixed-step continuous solver for your model, select `fixed-step` from the solver type list on the **Solver** pane. Then choose one of the following options from the adjacent integration method list.

- `ode5`, the Dormand-Prince formula
- `ode4`, RK4, the fourth-order Runge-Kutta formula
- `ode3`, the Bogacki-Shampine formula
- `ode2`, Heun's method, also known as the improved Euler formula
- `ode1`, Euler's method

Fixed-step discrete solver. Simulink provides a fixed-step solver that performs no integration. It is suitable for use in solving models that have no continuous states, including stateless models or models having only discrete states. To specify this solver, select `fixed-step` from the solver type list on the **Solver** pane. Then choose `discrete` from the adjacent integration method list.

Variable-step continuous solvers. These solvers decrease the simulation step size to increase accuracy when a system's continuous states are changing rapidly and increase the step size to save simulation time when a system's states are changing slowly. To specify a variable-step continuous solver for your model, select variable-step from the solver type list on the **Solver** pane. Then choose one of the following options from the adjacent integration method list.

- ode45 is based on an explicit Runge-Kutta (4,5) formula, the Dormand-Prince pair. It is a *one-step* solver; that is, in computing $y(t_n)$, it needs only the solution at the immediately preceding time point, $y(t_{n-1})$. In general, ode45 is the best solver to apply as a first try for most problems. For this reason, ode45 is the default solver used by Simulink for models with continuous states.

- ode23 is also based on an explicit Runge-Kutta (2,3) pair of Bogacki and Shampine. It can be more efficient than ode45 at crude tolerances and in the presence of mild stiffness. ode23 is a one-step solver.

- ode113 is a variable-order Adams-Bashforth-Moulton PECE solver. It can be more efficient than ode45 at stringent tolerances. ode113 is a *multistep* solver; that is, it normally needs the solutions at several preceding time points to compute the current solution.

- ode15s is a variable order solver based on the numerical differentiation formulas (NDFs). These are related to but are more efficient than the backward differentiation formulas, BDFs (also known as Gear's method). Like ode113, ode15s is a multistep method solver. If you suspect that a problem is stiff, or if ode45 failed or was very inefficient, try ode15s.

- ode23s is based on a modified Rosenbrock formula of order 2. Because it is a one-step solver, it can be more efficient than ode15s at crude tolerances. It can solve some kinds of stiff problems for which ode15s is not effective.

- ode23t is an implementation of the trapezoidal rule using a "free" interpolant. Use this solver if the problem is only moderately stiff and you need a solution without numerical damping.

- ode23tb is an implementation of TR-BDF2, an implicit Runge-Kutta formula with a first stage that is a trapezoidal rule step and a second stage that is a backward differentiation formula of order two. By construction, the same iteration matrix is used in evaluating both stages. Like ode23s, this solver can be more efficient than ode15s at crude tolerances.

Note For a *stiff* problem, solutions can change on a time scale that is very short compared to the interval of integration, but the solution of interest changes on a much longer time scale. Methods not designed for stiff problems are ineffective on intervals where the solution changes slowly because they use time steps small enough to resolve the fastest possible change. Jacobian matrices are generated numerically for ode15s and ode23s. For more information, see Shampine, L. F., *Numerical Solution of Ordinary Differential Equations*, Chapman & Hall, 1994.

Variable-Step Discrete Solver. Simulink provides a variable-step discrete solver that does no integration but does do zero-crossing detection (see "Zero-Crossing Detection" on page 3-14). Use this solver for models that have no continuous states and that have continuous signals requiring zero-crossing detection and/or have discrete blocks that operate at different sample times. Simulink uses this solver by default if you did not specify the fixed-step discrete solver and your model has no continuous states.

Simulink's fixed-step discrete solver advances the simulation by fixed-size time steps. As a result, it can take a step even when nothing is happening in the model. By contrast, Simulink's variable-step solver does not have to take a time step when nothing is happening in the model. Instead, it can adjust the step size to advance the simulation to the next point where something significant happens. Depending on the model, this can greatly reduce the number of steps and hence the time required to simulate a model.

The follow multirate model illustrates how the variable-step solver can shorten simulation time.

This model generates outputs at two different rates, every 0.5 second and every 0.75 second. To capture both outputs, the fixed-step solver must take a time step every 0.25 second (the *fundamental sample time* for the model).

```
[0.0 0.25 0.5 0.75 1.0 1.25 ...]
```

By contrast, the variable-step solver need take a step only when the model actually generates an output.

```
[0.0 0.5 0.75 1.0 1.5 2.0 2.25 ...]
```

This significantly reduces the number of time steps required to simulate the model.

Solver Options

The default solver parameters provide accurate and efficient results for most problems. In some cases, however, tuning the parameters can improve performance. (For more information about tuning these parameters, see "Improving Simulation Performance and Accuracy" on page 8-39.) You can tune the selected solver by changing parameter values on the **Solver** pane.

Step Sizes

For variable-step solvers, you can set the maximum and suggested initial step size parameters. By default, these parameters are automatically determined, indicated by the value auto.

For fixed-step solvers, you can set the fixed step size. The default is also auto.

Maximum step size. The **Max step size** parameter controls the largest time step the solver can take. The default is determined from the start and stop times.

$$h_{max} = \frac{t_{stop} - t_{start}}{50}$$

Generally, the default maximum step size is sufficient. If you are concerned about the solver's missing significant behavior, change the parameter to prevent the solver from taking too large a step. If the time span of the simulation is very long, the default step size might be too large for the solver to find the solution. Also, if your model contains periodic or nearly periodic behavior and you know the period, set the maximum step size to some fraction (such as 1/4) of that period.

In general, for more output points, change the refine factor, not the maximum step size. For more information, see "Refine output" on page 8-14.

Initial step size. By default, the solvers select an initial step size by examining the derivatives of the states at the start time. If the first step size is too large, the solver might step over important behavior. The initial step size parameter is a *suggested* first step size. The solver tries this step size but reduces it if error criteria are not satisfied.

Minimum step size. Specifies the smallest time step the solver can take. If the solver needs to take a smaller step to meet error tolerances, it issues a warning indicating the current effective relative tolerance. This parameter can be either a real number greater than zero or a two-element vector where the first element is the minimum step size and the second element is the maximum number of minimum step size warnings to be issued before issuing an error. Setting the second element to zero results in an error the first time the solver must take a step smaller than the specified minimum. This is equivalent to changing the minimum step size violation diagnostic to error on the **Diagnostics** panel. Setting the second element to -1 results in an unlimited number of warnings. This is also the default if the input is a scalar. The default values for this parameter are a minimum step size on the order of machine precision and an unlimited number of warnings.

Error Tolerances

The solvers use standard local error control techniques to monitor the error at each time step. During each time step, the solvers compute the state values at the end of the step and also determine the *local error*, the estimated error of these state values. They then compare the local error to the *acceptable error*, which is a function of the relative tolerance (*rtol*) and absolute tolerance (*atol*). If the error is greater than the acceptable error for *any* state, the solver reduces the step size and tries again:

- *Relative tolerance* measures the error relative to the size of each state. The relative tolerance represents a percentage of the state's value. The default, 1e-3, means that the computed state is accurate to within 0.1%.

- *Absolute tolerance* is a threshold error value. This tolerance represents the acceptable error as the value of the measured state approaches zero.

The error for the ith state, e_i, is required to satisfy

$$e_i \leq max(rtol \times |x_i|, atol_i)$$

The following figure shows a plot of a state and the regions in which the acceptable error is determined by the relative tolerance and the absolute tolerance.

If you specify auto (the default), Simulink sets the absolute tolerance for each state initially to 1e-6. As the simulation progresses, Simulink resets the absolute tolerance for each state to the maximum value that the state has assumed thus far times the relative tolerance for that state. Thus, if a state goes from 0 to 1 and reltol is 1e-3, then by the end of the simulation the abstol is set to 1e-3 also. If a state goes from 0 to 1000, then the abstol is set to 1.

If the computed setting is not suitable, you can determine an appropriate setting yourself. You might have to run a simulation more than once to determine an appropriate value for the absolute tolerance.

The Integrator, Transfer Fcn, State-Space, and Zero-Pole blocks allow you to specify absolute tolerance values for solving the model states that they compute or that determine their output. The absolute tolerance values that you specify for these blocks override the global settings in the **Simulation Parameters** dialog box. You might want to override the global setting in this way, if the global setting does not provide sufficient error control for all of your model's states, for example, because they vary widely in magnitude.

The Maximum Order for ode15s

The ode15s solver is based on NDF formulas of orders one through five. Although the higher order formulas are more accurate, they are less stable. If your model is stiff and requires more stability, reduce the maximum order to 2 (the highest order for which the NDF formula is A-stable). When you choose the ode15s solver, the dialog box displays this parameter.

As an alternative, you can try using the ode23s solver, which is a fixed-step, lower order (and A-stable) solver.

Multitasking Options

If you select a fixed-step solver, the **Solver** pane of the **Simulation Parameters** dialog box displays a **Mode** options list. The list allows you to select one of the following simulation modes.

MultiTasking. This mode issues an error if it detects an illegal sample rate transition between blocks, that is, a direct connection between blocks operating at different sample rates. In real-time multitasking systems, illegal sample rate transitions between tasks can result in a task's output not being available when needed by another task. By checking for such transitions, multitasking mode helps you to create valid models of real-world multitasking systems, where sections of your model represent concurrent tasks.

Use the Rate Transition block to eliminate illegal rate transitions from your model. For more information, see "Models with Multiple Sample Rates" in the online documentation for the Real-Time Workshop for more information.

SingleTasking. This mode does not check for sample rate transitions among blocks. This mode is useful when you are modeling a single-tasking system. In such systems, task synchronization is not an issue.

Auto. This option causes Simulink to use single-tasking mode if all blocks operate at the same rate and multitasking mode if the model contains blocks operating at different rates.

Output Options

The **Output options** area of the dialog box enables you to control how much output the simulation generates. You can choose from three options:

- Refine output
- Produce additional output
- Produce specified output only

Refine output. The Refine output choice provides additional output points when the simulation output is too coarse. This parameter provides an integer number of output points between time steps; for example, a refine factor of 2 provides output midway between the time steps, as well as at the steps. The default refine factor is 1.

To get smoother output, it is much faster to change the refine factor instead of reducing the step size. When the refine factor is changed, the solvers generate additional points by evaluating a continuous extension formula at those points. Changing the refine factor does not change the steps used by the solver.

The refine factor applies to variable-step solvers and is most useful when you are using ode45. The ode45 solver is capable of taking large steps; when graphing simulation output, you might find that output from this solver is not sufficiently smooth. If this is the case, run the simulation again with a larger refine factor. A value of 4 should provide much smoother results.

Note This option does not help the solver to locate zero crossings (see "Zero-Crossing Detection" on page 3-14).

Produce additional output. The Produce additional output choice enables you to specify directly those additional times at which the solver generates output. When you select this option, Simulink displays an **Output Times** field on the **Solver** pane. Enter a MATLAB expression in this field that evaluates to an additional time or a vector of additional times. The additional output is produced using a continuous extension formula at the additional times. Unlike the refine factor, this option changes the simulation step size so that time steps coincide with the times that you have specified for additional output.

Produce specified output only. The Produce specified output only choice provides simulation output *only* at the specified output times. This option changes the simulation step size so that time steps coincide with the times that you have specified for producing output. This choice is useful when you are comparing different simulations to ensure that the simulations produce output at the same times.

Comparing Output options. A sample simulation generates output at these times.

```
0, 2.5, 5, 8.5, 10
```

Choosing Refine output and specifying a refine factor of 2 generates output at these times.

```
0, 1.25, 2.5, 3.75, 5, 6.75, 8.5, 9.25, 10
```

Choosing the Produce additional output option and specifying [0:10] generates output at these times

```
0, 1, 2, 3, 4, 5, 6, 7, 8, 9, 10
```

and perhaps at additional times, depending on the step size chosen by the variable-step solver.

Choosing the Produce specified output only option and specifying [0:10] generates output at these times.

```
0, 1, 2, 3, 4, 5, 6, 7, 8, 9, 10
```

In general, you should specify output points as integers times a fundamental step size. For example,

```
[1:100]*0.01
```

is more accurate than

```
[1:0.01:100]
```

The Workspace I/O Pane

You can direct simulation output to workspace variables and get input and initial states from the workspace. On the **Simulation Parameters** dialog box, select the **Workspace I/O** tab. This pane appears.

Loading Input from the Base Workspace

Simulink can apply input from a model's base workspace to the model's top-level inports during a simulation run. To specify this option, select the **Input** box in the **Load from workspace** area of the **Workspace I/O** pane. Then, enter an external input specification (see below) in the adjacent edit box and select **Apply**.

The external (i.e., from workspace) input can take any of the following forms.

Array. To use this format, select **Input** in the **Load from workspace** pane and select the Array option from the **Format** list on the **Workspace I/O** pane. Selecting this option causes Simulink to evaluate the expression next to the **Input** check box and use the result as the input to the model.

The expression must evaluate to a real (noncomplex) matrix of data type double. The first column of the matrix must be a vector of times in ascending order. The remaining columns specify input values. In particular, each column represents the input for a different Inport block signal (in sequential order) and each row is the input value for the corresponding time point. Simulink linearly interpolates or extrapolates input values as necessary if the **Interpolate data** option is selected for the corresponding Inport.

The total number of columns of the input matrix must equal n + 1, where n is the total number of signals entering the model's inports.

The default input expression for a model is [t,u] and the default input format is Array. So if you define t and u in the base workspace, you need only select the **Input** option to input data from the model's base workspace. For example, suppose that a model has two inports, one of which accepts two signals and the other of which accepts one signal. Also, suppose that the base workspace defines u and t as follows.

```
t = (0:0.1:1)';
u = [sin(t), cos(t), 4*cos(t)];
```

Note The array input format allows you to load only real (noncomplex) scalar or vector data of type double. Use the structure format to input complex data, matrix (2-D) data, and/or data types other than double.

Structure with time. Simulink can read data from the workspace in the form of a structure whose name is specified in the **Input** text field. The input structure must have two top-level fields: time and signals. The time field contains a column vector of the simulation times. The signals field contains an array of substructures, each of which corresponds to a model input port.

Each signals substructure must contain two fields named values and dimensions, respectively. The values field must contain an array of inputs for the corresponding input port where each input corresponds to a time point specified by the time field. The dimensions field specifies the dimensions of the input. If each input is a scalar or vector (1-D array) value, the dimensions field must be a scalar value that specifies the length of the vector (1 for a scalar). If each input is a matrix (2-D array), the dimensions field must be a two-element vector whose first element specifies the number of rows in the matrix and whose second element specifies the number of columns.

If the inputs for a port are scalar or vector values, the values field must be an M-by-N array where M is the number of time points specified by the time field and N is the length of each vector value. For example, the following code creates an input structure for loading 11 time samples of a two-element signal vector of type `int8` into a model with a single input port.

```
a.time = (0:0.1:1)';
c1 = int8([0:1:10]');
c2 = int8([0:10:100]');
a.signals(1).values = [c1 c2];
a.signals(1).dimensions = 2;
```

To load this data into the model's inport, you would select the **Input** option on the **Workspace I/O** pane and enter a in the input expression field.

If the inputs for a port are matrices (2-D arrays), the `values` field must be an M-by-N-by-T array where M and N are the dimensions of each matrix input and T is the number of time points. For example, suppose that you want to input 51 time samples of a 4-by-5 matrix signal into one of your model's input ports. Then, the corresponding `dimensions` field of the workspace structure must equal [4 5] and the `values` array must have the dimensions 4-by-5-by-51.

As another example, consider the following model, which has two inputs.

Suppose that you want to input a sine wave into the first port and a cosine wave into the second port. To do this, define a vector, a, as follows, in the base workspace.

```
a.time = (0:0.1:1)';
a.signals(1).values = sin(a.time);
a.signals(1).dimensions = 1;
a.signals(2).values = cos(a.time);
a.signals(2).dimensions = 1;
```

Select the **Input** box for this model, enter a in the adjacent text field, and select `StructureWithTime` as the I/O format.

Note Simulink can read back simulation data saved to the workspace in the **Structure with time** output format. See "Structure with time" on page 8-22 for more information.

Structure. The **Structure** format is the same as the **Structure with time** format except that the time field is empty. For example, in the preceding example, you could set the time field as follows:

```
a.time = []
```

In this case, Simulink reads the input for the first time step from the first element of an inport's value array, the value for the second time step from the second element of the value array, etc.

Note Simulink can read back simulation data saved to the workspace in the **Structure** output format. See "Structure" on page 8-23 for more information.

Per-Port Structures. This format consists of a separate structure-with-time or structure-without-time for each port. Each port's input data structure has only one signals field. To specify this option, enter the names of the structures in the **Input** text field as a comma-separated list, in1, in2, ..., inN, where in1 is the data for your model's first port, in2 for the second inport, and so on.

Time Expression. The time expression can be any MATLAB expression that evaluates to a row vector equal in length to the number of signals entering the model's inports. For example, suppose that a model has one vector inport that accepts two signals. Furthermore, suppose that timefcn is a user-defined function that returns a row vector two elements long. The following are valid input time expressions for such a model.

```
'[3*sin(t), cos(2*t)]'
```

```
'4*timefcn(w*t)+7'
```

Simulink evaluates the expression at each step of the simulation, applying the resulting values to the model's inports. Note that Simulink defines the variable t when it runs the simulation. Also, you can omit the time variable in expressions for functions of one variable. For example, Simulink interprets the expression `sin` as `sin(t)`.

Saving Output to the Workspace

You can specify return variables by selecting the **Time**, **States**, and/or **Output** check boxes in the **Save to workspace** area of this dialog box pane. Specifying return variables causes Simulink to write values for the time, state, and output trajectories (as many as are selected) into the workspace.

To assign values to different variables, specify those variable names in the fields to the right of the check boxes. To write output to more than one variable, specify the variable names in a comma-separated list. Simulink saves the simulation times in the vector specified in the **Save to Workspace** area.

Note Simulink saves the output to the workspace at the base sample rate of the model. Use a To Workspace block if you want to save output at a different sample rate.

The **Save options** area enables you to specify the format and restrict the amount of output saved.

Format options for model states and outputs are listed below.

Array. If you select this option, Simulink saves a model's states and outputs in a state and output array, respectively.

The state matrix has the name specified in the **Save to Workspace** area (for example, `xout`). Each row of the state matrix corresponds to a time sample of the model's states. Each column corresponds to an element of a state. For example, suppose that your model has two continuous states, each of which is a two-element vector. Then the first two elements of each row of the state matrix contains a time sample of the first state vector. The last two elements of each row contain a time sample of the second state vector.

The model output matrix has the name specified in the **Save to Workspace** area (for example, `yout`). Each column corresponds to a model outport, each row to the outputs at a specific time.

Note You can use array format to save your model's outputs and states only if the outputs are either all scalars or all vectors (or all matrices for states), are either all real or all complex, and are all of the same data type. Use the Structure or StructureWithTime output formats (see the following) if your model's outputs and states do not meet these conditions.

Structure with time. If you select this format, Simulink saves the model's states and outputs in structures having the names specified in the **Save to Workspace** area (for example, xout and yout).

The structure used to save outputs has two top-level fields: time and signals. The time field contains a vector of the simulation times. The signals field contains an array of substructures, each of which corresponds to a model outport. Each substructure has four fields: values, dimensions, label, and blockName. The values field contains the outputs for the corresponding outport. If the outputs are scalars or vectors, the values field is a matrix each of whose rows represents an output at the time specified by the corresponding element of the time vector. If the outputs are matrix (2-D) values, the values field is a 3-D array of dimensions M-by-N-by-T where M-by-N is the dimensions of the output signal and T is the number of output samples. If T = 1, MATLAB drops the last dimension. Therefore, the values field is an M-by-N matrix. The dimensions field specifies the dimensions of the output signal. The label field specifies the label of the signal connected to the outport or the type of state (continuous or discrete). The blockName field specifies the name of the corresponding outport or block with states.

The structure used to save states has a similar organization. The states structure has two top-level fields: time and signals. The time field contains a vector of the simulation times. The signals field contains an array of substructures, each of which corresponds to one of the model's states. Each signals structure has four fields: values, dimension, label, and blockName. The values field contains time samples of a state of the block specified by the blockName field. The label field for built-in blocks indicates the type of state: either CSTATE (continuous state) or DSTATE (discrete state). For S-Function blocks, the label contains whatever name is assigned to the state by the S-Function block.

The time samples of a state are stored in the `values` field as a matrix of values. Each row corresponds to a time sample. Each element of a row corresponds to an element of the state. If the state is a matrix, the matrix is stored in the `values` array in column-major order. For example, suppose that the model includes a 2-by-2 matrix state and that Simulink logs 51 samples of the state during a simulation run. The `values` field for this state would contain a 51-by-4 matrix where each row corresponds to a time sample of the state and where the first two elements of each row correspond to the first column of the sample and the last two elements correspond to the second column of the sample.

Structure. This format is the same as the preceding except that Simulink does not store simulation times in the `time` field of the saved structure.

Per-Port Structures. This format consists of a separate structure-with-time or structure-without-time for each output port. Each output data structure has only one `signals` field. To specify this option, enter the names of the structures in the **Output** text field as a comma-separated list, `out1, out2, ..., outN`, where `out1` is the data for your model's first port, `out2` for the second inport, and so on.

Saving data to the workspace can slow down the simulation and consume memory. To avoid this, you can limit the number of samples saved to the most recent samples or you can skip samples by applying a decimation factor. To set a limit on the number of data samples saved, select the check box labeled **Limit data points to last** and specify the number of samples to save. To apply a decimation factor, enter a value in the field to the right of the **Decimation** label. For example, a value of 2 saves every other point generated.

Loading and Saving States

Initial conditions, which are applied to the system at the start of the simulation, are generally set in the blocks. You can override initial conditions set in the blocks by specifying them in the **States** area of this pane.

You can also save the final states for the current simulation run and apply them to a subsequent simulation run. This feature can be useful when you want to save a steady-state solution and restart the simulation at that known state. The states are saved in the format that you select in the **Save options** area of the **Workspace I/O** pane.

To save the final states (the values of the states at the termination of the simulation), select the **Final State** check box and enter a variable in the adjacent edit field.

To load states, select the **Initial State** check box and specify the name of a variable that contains the initial state values. This variable can be a matrix or a structure of the same form as is used to save final states. This allows Simulink to set the initial states for the current session to the final states saved in a previous session, using the **Structure** or **Structure with time** format.

If the check box is not selected or the state array is empty ([ ]), Simulink uses the initial conditions defined in the blocks.

The Diagnostics Pane

You can indicate the desired action for many types of events or conditions that can be encountered during a simulation by selecting the **Diagnostics** tab on the **Simulation Parameters** dialog box. This dialog box appears.

The dialog box includes the following options.

Consistency Checking

Consistency checking is a debugging tool that validates certain assumptions made by Simulink ODE solvers. Its main use is to make sure that S-functions adhere to the same rules as Simulink built-in blocks. Because consistency checking results in a significant decrease in performance (up to 40%), it should generally be set to off. Use consistency checking to validate your S-functions and to help you determine the cause of unexpected simulation results.

To perform efficient integration, Simulink saves (caches) certain values from one time step for use in the next time step. For example, the derivatives at the end of a time step can generally be reused at the start of the next time step. The solvers take advantage of this to avoid redundant derivative calculations.

Another purpose of consistency checking is to ensure that blocks produce constant output when called with a given value of t (time). This is important for the stiff solvers (ode23s and ode15s) because, while calculating the Jacobian, the block's output functions can be called many times at the same value of t.

When consistency checking is enabled, Simulink recomputes the appropriate values and compares them to the cached values. If the values are not the same, a consistency error occurs. Simulink compares computed values for these quantities:

- Outputs
- Zero crossings
- Derivatives
- States

Bounds checking

This option causes Simulink to check whether a block writes outside the memory allocated to it during simulation. Typically this can happen only if your model includes a user-written S-function that has a bug. If enabled, this check is performed for every block in the model every time the block is executed. As a result, enabling this option slows down model execution considerably. Thus, to avoid slowing down model execution needlessly, you should enable the option only if you suspect that your model contains a user-written S-function that has a bug. See *Writing S-Functions* for more information on using this option.

Configuration options

This control lists abnormal types of events that can occur during execution of the model. For each event type, you can choose whether you want no message, a warning message, or an error message. A warning message does not terminate a simulation, but an error message does.

Event	Description
`-1 sample time in source`	A source block (e.g., a Sine Wave block) specifies a sample time of -1.
`Algebraic loop`	Simulink detected an algebraic loop while simulating the model. See "Algebraic Loops" on page 3-18 for more information. If you set this option to `Error`, Simulink displays an error message and highlights the portion of the block diagram that comprises the loop (see "Highlighting Algebraic Loops" on page 3-22).
`Block priority violation`	Simulink detected a block priority specification error while simulating the model.
`Check for singular matrix`	The Product block detected a singular matrix while inverting one of its inputs in matrix multiplication mode.
`Data overflow`	The value of a signal or parameter is too large to be represented by the signal or parameter's data type.
`Discrete used as continuous`	The Unit Delay block, which is a discrete block, inherits a continuous sample time from the block connected to its input.
`int32 to float conversion`	A 32-bit integer value was converted to a floating-point value. Such a conversion can result in a loss of precision.
`Invalid FcnCall Connection`	Simulink has detected an incorrect use of a Function-Call subsystem in your model (see the "Function-call systems" examples in the Simulink "Subsystem Semantics" library for examples of invalid uses of Function-Call subsystems. Disabling this error message can lead to invalid simulation results.

Event	Description (Continued)
Min step size violation	The next simulation step is smaller than the minimum step size specified for the model. This can occur if the specified error tolerance for the model requires a step size smaller than the specified minimum step size. See "Step Sizes" on page 8-11 and "Error Tolerances" on page 8-12 for more information.
Multitask rate transition	An invalid rate transition occurred between two blocks operating in multitasking mode (see "Multitasking Options" on page 8-14).
Parameter downcast	Computation of the output of the block required converting the parameter's specified type to a type having a smaller range of values (e.g., from uint32 to uint8). This diagnostic applies only to named tunable parameters.
Parameter overflow	The data type of the parameter could not accommodate the parameter's value.
Parameter precision loss	Computation of the output of the block required converting the specified data type of the parameter to a less precise data type (e.g., from double to uint8).
S-function upgrades needed	A block was encountered that has not been upgraded to use features of the current release.
Signal label mismatch	The simulation encountered virtual signals that have a common source signal but different labels (see "Virtual Signals" on page 7-3).
SingleTask rate transition	A rate transition occurred between two blocks operating in single-tasking mode (see "Multitasking Options" on page 8-14).
Unconnected block input	Model contains a block with an unconnected input.

Event	Description (Continued)
Unconnected block output	Model contains a block with an unconnected output.
Unconnected line	Model contains an unconnected line.
Underspecified data types	Simulink could not infer the data type of a signal during data type propagation.
Unneeded type conversions	A Data Type Conversion block is used where no type conversion is necessary.
Vector/Matrix conversion	A vector-to-matrix or matrix-to-vector conversion occurred at a block input (see "Vector or Matrix Input Conversion Rules" on page 7-8).

The Advanced Pane

The **Advanced** pane allows you to set various options that affect simulation performance.

Model parameter configuration

Inline parameters. By default you can modify ("tune") many block parameters during simulation (see "Tunable Parameters" on page 3-5). Selecting this option makes all parameters nontunable by default. Making parameters nontunable allows Simulink to move blocks whose outputs depend only on block parameter values outside the simulation loop, thereby speeding up simulation of the model and execution of code generated from the model. When this option is selected, Simulink disables the parameter controls of the block dialog boxes for the blocks in your model to prevent you from accidentally modifying the block parameters.

Simulink allows you to override the **Inline parameters** option for parameters whose values are defined by variables in the MATLAB workspace. To specify that such a parameter remain tunable, specify the parameter as global in the **Model Parameter Configuration** dialog box (see "Model Parameter Configuration Dialog Box" on page 8-33). To display the dialog, select the adjacent **Configure** button. To tune a global parameter, change the value of the corresponding workspace variable and choose **Update Diagram (Ctrl+D)** from the Simulink **Edit** menu.

Note You cannot tune inlined parameters in code generated from a model. However, when simulating a model, you can tune an inlined parameter if its value derives from a workspace variable. For example, suppose that a model has a Gain block whose **Gain** parameter is inlined and equals a, where a is a variable defined in the model's workspace. When simulating the model, Simulink disables the **Gain** parameter field, thereby preventing you from using the block's dialog box to change the gain. However, you can still tune the gain by changing the value of a at the MATLAB command line and updating the diagram.

Optimizations

Block reduction. Replaces a group of blocks with a synthesized block, thereby speeding up execution of the model.

Boolean logic signals. Causes blocks that accept Boolean signals to require Boolean signals. If this option is off, blocks that accept inputs of type `boolean` also accept inputs of type `double`. For example, consider the following model.

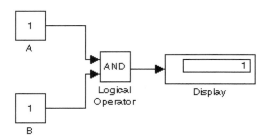

This model connects signals of type double to a Logical Operator block, which accepts inputs of type boolean. If the Boolean logic signals option is on, this model generates an error when executed. If the Boolean logic signals option is off, this model runs without error.

Note This option allows the current version of Simulink to run models that were created by earlier versions of Simulink that supported only signals of type double.

Conditional input branch. This optimization applies to models containing Switch and Multiport Switch blocks. When enabled, this optimization executes only the blocks required to compute the control input and the data input selected by the control input at each time step for each Switch or Multiport Switch block in the model. Similarly, code generated from the model by Real-Time Workshop executes only the code needed to compute the control input and the selected data input. This optimization speeds simulation and execution of code generated from the model.

At the beginning of the simulation or code generation, Simulink examines each signal path feeding a switch block data input to determine the portion of the path that can be optimized. The optimizable portion of the path is that part of the signal path that stretches from the corresponding data input back to the first block that is a nonvirtual subsystem, has continuous or discrete states, or detects zero crossings.

Simulink encloses the optimizable portion of the signal path in an invisible atomic subsystem. During simulation, if a switch data input is not selected, Simulink executes only the nonoptimizable portion of the signal path feeding the input. If the data input is selected, Simulink executes both the nonoptimizable and the optimizable portion of the input signal path.

Parameter pooling. This option is used for code generation (see the Real-Time Workshop documentation for more information). Leave this option on if you are not doing code generation.

Signal storage reuse. Causes Simulink to reuse memory buffers allocated to store block input and output signals. If this option is off, Simulink allocates a separate memory buffer for each block's outputs. This can substantially increase the amount of memory required to simulate large models, so you should select this option only when you need to debug a model. In particular, you should disable signal storage reuse if you need to

- Debug a C-MEX S-function
- Use a floating Scope or Display block to inspect signals in a model that you are debugging

Simulink opens an error dialog if Signal storage reuse is enabled and you attempt to use a floating Scope or Display block to display a signal whose buffer has been reused.

Zero-crossing detection. Enables zero-crossing detection during variable-step simulation of the model. For most models, this speeds up simulation by enabling the solver to take larger time steps. If a model has extreme dynamic changes, disabling this option can speed up the simulation but can also decrease the accuracy of simulation results. See "Zero-Crossing Detection" on page 3-14 for more information.

You can override this optimization on a block-by-block basis for the following types of blocks.

Abs	Integrator	Step
Backlash	MinMax	Switch
Dead Zone	Relay	Switch Case
Enable	Relational Operator	Trigger

Hit Crossing   Saturation

If   Sign

To override zero-crossing detection for an instance of one of these blocks, open the block's parameter dialog box and uncheck the **Enable zero crossing detection** option. You can enable or disable zero-crossing selectively for these blocks only if zero-crossing detection is enabled globally, i.e., `Zero-crossing optimization` is selected on the **Advanced** pane of the **Simulation Parameters** dialog box.

Model Verification block control

This parameter allows you to enable or disable model verification blocks in the current model either globally or locally. Select one of the following options:

- `Use local settings`

  Enables or disables blocks based on the value of the **Enable Assertion** parameter of each block. If a block's **Enable Assertion** parameter is on, the block is enabled; otherwise, the block is disabled.

- `Enable all`

  Enables all model verification blocks in the model regardless of the settings of their **Enable Assertion** parameters.

- `Disable all`

  Disables all model verification blocks in the model regardless of the settings of their **Enable Assertion** parameters.

Model Parameter Configuration Dialog Box

The **Model Parameter Configuration** dialog box allows you to override the **Inline parameters** option (see "Model parameter configuration" on page 8-28) for selected parameters.

The dialog box has the following controls.

Source list. Displays a list of workspace variables. The options are

- MATLAB workspace

  List all variables in the MATLAB workspace that have numeric values.

- Referenced workspace variables

  List only those variables referenced by the model.

Refresh list. Updates the source list. Click this button if you have added a variable to the workspace since the last time the list was displayed.

Add to table. Adds the variables selected in the source list to the adjacent table of tunable parameters.

New. Defines a new parameter and adds it to the list of tunable parameters. Use this button to create tunable parameters that are not yet defined in the MATLAB workspace.

Note This option does not create the corresponding variable in the MATLAB workspace. You must create the variable yourself.

Storage class. Used for code generation. See the Real-Time Workshop documentation for more information.

Storage type qualifier. Used for code generation. See the Real-Time Workshop documentation for more information.

Production Hardware Characteristics

This setting is intended for use in modeling, simulating, and generating code for digital systems. It allows you to specify the sizes of the data types supported by the system being modeled. Simulink uses this information to automate the choice of data types for signals output by some blocks, e.g., the Product and Gain blocks.

Select one of the following settings from the list:

- `Microprocessor`

  Specifies that this model represents a microprocessor-based digital system whose integer word lengths correspond to the C data types listed in the control below the **Production hardware characteristics** list.

  The entry for each C data type specifies the length in bits of the corresponding microprocessor word. You can change the length by selecting the data type and entering a new length in the adjacent **Value** field.

- `Unconstrained integer sizes`

  Specifies that the hardware implementation of the modeled system imposes no size constraints on the choice of integer data types used to perform computations. This might be the case, for example, if the production hardware is intended to be a custom integrated circuit.

Diagnosing Simulation Errors

If errors occur during a simulation, Simulink halts the simulation, opens the subsystems that caused the error (if necessary), and displays the errors in the Simulation Diagnostics Viewer. The following section explains how to use the viewer to determine the cause of the errors.

Simulation Diagnostic Viewer

The viewer comprises an Error Summary pane and an Error Message pane.

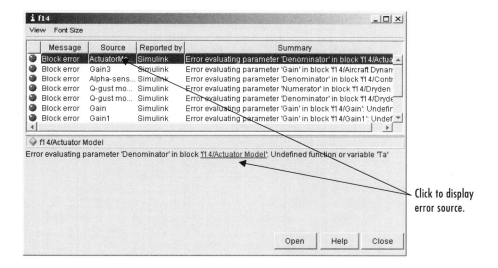

Click to display error source.

Error Summary Pane

The upper pane lists the errors that caused Simulink to terminate the simulation. The pane displays the following information for each error.

Message. Message type (for example, block error, warning, log)

Source. Name of the model element (for example, a block) that caused the error

Reported by. Component that reported the error (for example, Simulink, Stateflow, Real-Time Workshop, etc.)

Summary. Error message, abbreviated to fit in the column

You can remove any of these columns of information to make more room for the others. To remove a column, select the viewer's **View** menu and uncheck the corresponding item.

Error Message Pane

The lower pane initially contains the contents of the first error message listed in the top pane. You can display the contents of other messages by clicking their entries in the upper pane.

In addition to displaying the Diagnostic Viewer, Simulink also opens (if necessary) the subsystem that contains the first error source and highlights the source.

You can display the sources of other errors by clicking anywhere in the error message in the upper pane, by clicking the name of the error source in the error message (highlighted in blue), or by selecting the **Open** button on the viewer.

Changing Font Size

To change the size of the font used to display errors, select **Font Size** from the viewer's menu bar. A menu of font sizes appears. Select the desired font size from the menu.

Creating Custom Simulation Error Messages

The Simulink Diagnostic Viewer displays the output of any instance of the MATLAB error function executed during a simulation, including instances invoked by block or model callbacks or S-functions that you create or that are executed by the MATLAB Function block. Thus, you can use the MATLAB error function in callbacks and S-functions or in the MATLAB Function block to create simulation error messages specific to your application.

For example, in the following model,

the MATLAB Function block invokes the following function

```
function y=check_signal(x)
  if x<0
    error('Signal is negative.');
  else
    y=x;
  end
```

Executing this model displays an error message in the Simulation Diagnostics viewer.

Including Hyperlinks in Error Messages

You can include hyperlinks to blocks, text files, and directories.

To include a hyperlink to a block, path, or directory, include the item's path in the error message enclosed in quotation marks, e.g.,

- `error ('Error evaluating parameter in block "mymodel/Mu"')`

  displays a text hyperlink to the block Mu in the current model in the error message. Clicking the hyperlink displays the block in the model window.

- error ('Error reading data from "c:/work/test.data"')

  displays a text hyperlink to the file test.data in the error message. Clicking the link displays the file in your preferred MATLAB editor.

- error ('Could not find data in directory "c:/work"')

  displays a text hyperlink to the c:/work directory. Clicking the link opens a system command window (shell) and sets its working directory to c:/work.

Note The text hyperlink is enabled only if the corresponding block exists in the current model or if the corresponding file or directory exists on the user's system.

Improving Simulation Performance and Accuracy

Simulation performance and accuracy can be affected by many things, including the model design and choice of simulation parameters.

The solvers handle most model simulations accurately and efficiently with their default parameter values. However, some models yield better results if you adjust solver and simulation parameters. Also, if you know information about your model's behavior, your simulation results can be improved if you provide this information to the solver.

Speeding Up the Simulation

Slow simulation speed can have many causes. Here are a few:

- Your model includes a MATLAB Fcn block. When a model includes a MATLAB Fcn block, the MATLAB interpreter is called at each time step, drastically slowing down the simulation. Use the built-in Fcn block or Math Function block whenever possible.

- Your model includes an M-file S-function. M-file S-functions also cause the MATLAB interpreter to be called at each time step. Consider either converting the S-function to a subsystem or to a C-MEX file S-function.

- Your model includes a Memory block. Using a Memory block causes the variable-order solvers (ode15s and ode113) to be reset back to order 1 at each time step.

- The maximum step size is too small. If you changed the maximum step size, try running the simulation again with the default value (auto).

- Did you ask for too much accuracy? The default relative tolerance (0.1% accuracy) is usually sufficient. For models with states that go to zero, if the absolute tolerance parameter is too small, the simulation can take too many steps around the near-zero state values. See the discussion of error in "Error Tolerances" on page 8-12.

- The time scale might be too long. Reduce the time interval.

- The problem might be stiff but you are using a nonstiff solver. Try using ode15s.

- The model uses sample times that are not multiples of each other. Mixing sample times that are not multiples of each other causes the solver to take small enough steps to ensure sample time hits for all sample times.

- The model contains an algebraic loop. The solutions to algebraic loops are iteratively computed at every time step. Therefore, they severely degrade performance. For more information, see "Algebraic Loops" on page 3-18.
- Your model feeds a Random Number block into an Integrator block. For continuous systems, use the Band-Limited White Noise block in the Sources library.

Improving Simulation Accuracy

To check your simulation accuracy, run the simulation over a reasonable time span. Then, either reduce the relative tolerance to 1e-4 (the default is 1e-3) or reduce the absolute tolerance and run it again. Compare the results of both simulations. If the results are not significantly different, you can feel confident that the solution has converged.

If the simulation misses significant behavior at its start, reduce the initial step size to ensure that the simulation does not step over the significant behavior.

If the simulation results become unstable over time,

- Your system might be unstable.
- If you are using ode15s, you might need to restrict the maximum order to 2 (the maximum order for which the solver is A-stable) or try using the ode23s solver.

If the simulation results do not appear to be accurate,

- For a model that has states whose values approach zero, if the absolute tolerance parameter is too large, the simulation takes too few steps around areas of near-zero state values. Reduce this parameter value or adjust it for individual states in the Integrator dialog box.
- If reducing the absolute tolerances does not sufficiently improve the accuracy, reduce the size of the relative tolerance parameter to reduce the acceptable error and force smaller step sizes and more steps.

9

Analyzing Simulation Results

The following sections explain how to use Simulink tools for analyzing the results of simulations.

Viewing Output Trajectories

Output trajectories from Simulink can be plotted using one of three methods:

- Feed a signal into either a Scope or an XY Graph block.
- Write output to return variables and use MATLAB plotting commands.
- Write output to the workspace using To Workspace blocks and plot the results using MATLAB plotting commands.

Using the Scope Block

You can use display output trajectories on a Scope block during a simulation. This simple model shows an example of the use of the Scope block.

The display on the Scope shows the output trajectory. The Scope block enables you to zoom in on an area of interest or save the data to the workspace.

The XY Graph block enables you to plot one signal against another.

Using Return Variables

By returning time and output histories, you can use MATLAB plotting commands to display and annotate the output trajectories.

The block labeled Out is an Outport block from the Signals & Systems library. The output trajectory, yout, is returned by the integration solver. For more information, see "The Workspace I/O Pane" on page 8-17.

You can also run this simulation from the **Simulation** menu by specifying variables for the time, output, and states on the **Workspace I/O** pane of the **Simulation Parameters** dialog box. You can then plot these results using

```
plot(tout,yout)
```

Using the To Workspace Block

The To Workspace block can be used to return output trajectories to the MATLAB workspace. The model below illustrates this use.

The variables y and t appear in the workspace when the simulation is complete. You store the time vector by feeding a Clock block into a To Workspace block. You can also acquire the time vector by entering a variable name for the time on the **Workspace I/O** pane of the **Simulation Parameters** dialog box, for menu-driven simulations, or by returning it using the sim command (see "The Workspace I/O Pane" on page 8-17 for more information).

The To Workspace block can accept an array input, with each input element's trajectory stored in the resulting workspace variable.

Linearizing Models

Simulink provides the `linmod` and `dlinmod` functions to extract linear models in the form of the state-space matrices A, B, C, and D. State-space matrices describe the linear input-output relationship as

$$\dot{x} = Ax + Bu$$
$$y = Cx + Du$$

where x, u, and y are state, input, and output vectors, respectively. For example, the following model is called `lmod`.

To extract the linear model of this Simulink system, enter this command.

```
[A,B,C,D] = linmod('lmod')
A =
      -2     -1     -1
       1      0      0
       0      1     -1
B =
       1
       0
       0
C =
       0      1      0
       0      0     -1
D =
       0
       1
```

Inputs and outputs must be defined using Inport and Outport blocks from the Signals & Systems library. Source and sink blocks do not act as inputs and outputs. Inport blocks can be used in conjunction with source blocks, using a Sum block. Once the data is in the state-space form or converted to an LTI object, you can apply functions in the Control System Toolbox for further analysis:

- Conversion to an LTI object

  ```
  sys = ss(A,B,C,D);
  ```

- Bode phase and magnitude frequency plot

  ```
  bode(A,B,C,D) or bode(sys)
  ```

- Linearized time response

  ```
  step(A,B,C,D) or step(sys)
  impulse(A,B,C,D) or impulse(sys)
  lsim(A,B,C,D,u,t) or lsim(sys,u,t)
  ```

You can use other functions in the Control System Toolbox and Robust Control Toolbox for linear control system design.

When the model is nonlinear, an operating point can be chosen at which to extract the linearized model. The nonlinear model is also sensitive to the perturbation sizes at which the model is extracted. These must be selected to balance the tradeoff between truncation and roundoff error. Extra arguments to linmod specify the operating point and perturbation points.

```
[A,B,C,D] = linmod('sys', x, u, pert, xpert, upert)
```

For discrete systems or mixed continuous and discrete systems, use the function dlinmod for linearization. This has the same calling syntax as linmod except that the second right-hand argument must contain a sample time at which to perform the linearization.

Using linmod to linearize a model that contains Derivative or Transport Delay blocks can be troublesome. Before linearizing, replace these blocks with specially designed blocks that avoid the problems. These blocks are in the Simulink Extras library in the Linearization sublibrary. You access the Extras library by opening the Blocksets & Toolboxes icon:

- For the Derivative block, use the Switched derivative for linearization.
- For the Transport Delay block, use the Switched transport delay for linearization. (Using this block requires that you have the Control System Toolbox.)

When using a Derivative block, you can also try to incorporate the derivative term in other blocks. For example, if you have a Derivative block in series with a Transfer Fcn block, it is better implemented (although this is not always possible) with a single Transfer Fcn block of the form

$$\frac{s}{s+a}$$

In this example, the blocks on the left of this figure can be replaced by the block on the right.

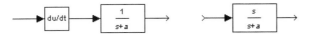

Finding Steady-State Points

The Simulink trim function uses a Simulink model to determine steady-state points of a dynamic system that satisfy input, output, and state conditions that you specify. Consider, for example, this model, called lmod.

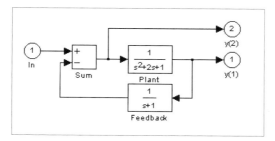

You can use the trim function to find the values of the input and the states that set both outputs to 1. First, make initial guesses for the state variables (x) and input values (u), then set the desired value for the output (y).

```
x = [0; 0; 0];
u = 0;
y = [1; 1];
```

Use index variables to indicate which variables are fixed and which can vary.

```
ix = [];        % Don't fix any of the states
iu = [];        % Don't fix the input
iy = [1;2];     % Fix both output 1 and output 2
```

Invoking trim returns the solution. Your results might differ because of roundoff error.

```
[x,u,y,dx] = trim('lmod',x,u,y,ix,iu,iy)

x =
    0.0000
    1.0000
    1.0000
u =
    2
y =
    1.0000
```

```
        1.0000
dx  =
      1.0e 015  *
      -0.2220
      -0.0227
       0.3331
```

Note that there might be no solution to equilibrium point problems. If that is the case, `trim` returns a solution that minimizes the maximum deviation from the desired result after first trying to set the derivatives to zero. For a description of the `trim` syntax, see `trim` in the Simulink online Help.

Creating Masked Subsystems

This section explains how to create custom user interfaces (masks) for Simulink subsystems.

About Masks

A mask is a custom user interface for a subsystem that hides the subsystem's contents, making it appear to the user as an atomic block with its own icon and parameter dialog box. The Simulink Mask Editor enables you to create a mask for any subsystem. Masking a subsystem allows you to

- Replace the parameter dialogs of a subsystem and its contents with a single parameter dialog with its own block description, parameter prompts, and help text
- Replace a subsystem's standard icon with a custom icon that depicts its purpose
- Prevent unintended modification of subsystems by hiding their contents behind a mask
- Create a custom block by encapsulating a block diagram that defines the block's behavior in a masked subsystem and then placing the masked subsystem in a library

Mask Features

Masks can include any of the following features.

Mask Icon

The mask icon replaces a subsystem's standard icon, i.e., it appears in a block diagram in place of the standard icon for a subsystem block. Simulink uses MATLAB code that you supply to draw the custom icon. You can use any MATLAB drawing command in the icon code. This gives you great flexibility in designing an icon for a masked subsystem.

Mask Parameters

Simulink allows you to define a set of user-settable parameters for a masked subsystem. Simulink stores the value of a parameter in the mask workspace (see "Mask Workspace" on page 10-3) as the value of a variable whose name you specify. These associated variables allow you to link mask parameters to specific parameters of blocks inside a masked subsystem (internal parameters) such that setting a mask parameter sets the associated block parameter (see "Linking Mask Parameters to Block Parameters" on page 10-27).

Mask Parameter Dialog Box

The mask parameter dialog box contains controls that enable a user to set the values of the masks parameters and hence the values of any internal parameters linked to the mask parameters.

The mask parameter dialog box replaces the subsystem's standard parameter dialog box, i.e., clicking on the masked subsystem's icon causes the mask dialog box to appear instead of the standard parameter dialog box for a Subsystem block. You can customize every feature of the mask dialog box, including which parameters appear on the dialog box, the order in which they appear, parameter prompts, the controls used to edit the parameters, and the parameter callbacks (code used to process parameter values entered by the user).

Mask Initialization Code

The initialization code is MATLAB code that you specify and that Simulink runs to initialize the masked subsystem at the start of a simulation run. You can use the initialization code to set the initial values of the masked subsystem's mask parameters.

Mask Workspace

Simulink associates a MATLAB workspace with each masked subsystem that you create. Simulink stores the current values of the subsystem's parameters in the workspace as well as any variables created by the block's initialization code and parameter callbacks. You can use model and mask workspace variables to initialize a masked subsystem and to set the values of blocks inside the masked subsystem, subject to the following rules.

- A block parameter expression can refer only to variables defined in the subsystem or nested subsystems that contain the block or in the model's workspace.

- A valid reference to a variable defined on more than one level in the model hierarchy resolves to the most local definition.

  For example, suppose that model M contains masked subsystem A, which contains masked subsystem B. Further suppose that B refers to a variable x that exists in both A's and M's workspaces. In this case, the reference resolves to the value in A's workspace.

- A masked subsystem's initialization code can refer only to variables in its local workspace.

Creating Masks

See "Masking a Subsystem" on page 10-10 for an overview of the process of creating a masked subsystem. See "Masked Subsystem Example" on page 10-5 for an example of the process.

Masked Subsystem Example

This simple subsystem models the equation for a line, y = mx + b.

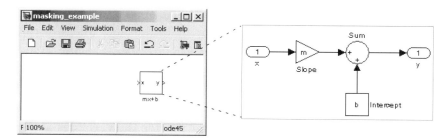

Ordinarily, when you double-click a Subsystem block, the Subsystem block opens, displaying its blocks in a separate window. The mx + b subsystem contains a Gain block, named Slope, whose **Gain** parameter is specified as m, and a Constant block, named Intercept, whose **Constant value** parameter is specified as b. These parameters represent the slope and intercept of a line.

This example creates a custom dialog box and icon for the subsystem. One dialog box contains prompts for both the slope and the intercept. After you create the mask, double-click the Subsystem block to open the mask dialog box. The mask dialog box and icon look like this:

A user enters values for **Slope** and **Intercept** in the mask dialog box. Simulink makes these values available to all the blocks in the underlying subsystem. Masking this subsystem creates a self-contained functional unit with its own application-specific parameters, **Slope** and **Intercept**. The mask maps these *mask parameters* to the generic parameters of the underlying blocks. The complexity of the subsystem is encapsulated by a new interface that has the look and feel of a built-in Simulink block.

To create a mask for this subsystem, you need to

- Specify the prompts for the mask dialog box parameters. In this example, the mask dialog box has prompts for the slope and intercept.
- Specify the variable name used to store the value of each parameter.
- Enter the documentation of the block, consisting of the block description and the block help text.
- Specify the drawing command that creates the block icon.
- Specify the commands that provide the variables needed by the drawing command (there are none in this example).

Creating Mask Dialog Box Prompts

To create the mask for this subsystem, select the Subsystem block and choose **Mask Subsystem** from the **Edit** menu.

This example primarily uses the Mask Editor's **Parameters** pane to create the masked subsystem's dialog box.

The Mask Editor enables you to specify these attributes of a mask parameter:

- Prompt, the text label that describes the parameter
- Control type, the style of user interface control that determines how parameter values are entered or selected
- Variable, the name of the variable that stores the parameter value

Generally, it is convenient to refer to masked parameters by their prompts. In this example, the parameter associated with slope is referred to as the **Slope** parameter, and the parameter associated with intercept is referred to as the **Intercept** parameter.

The slope and intercept are defined as edit controls. This means that the user types values into edit fields in the mask dialog box. These values are stored in variables in the *mask workspace*. Masked blocks can access variables only in the mask workspace. In this example, the value entered for the slope is assigned to the variable m. The Slope block in the masked subsystem gets the value for the slope parameter from the mask workspace. This figure shows how the slope parameter definitions in the Mask Editor map to the actual mask dialog box parameters.

After you create the mask parameters for slope and intercept, click the **OK** button. Then double-click the Subsystem block to open the newly constructed dialog box. Enter 3 for the **Slope** and 2 for the **Intercept** parameter.

Creating the Block Description and Help Text

The mask type, block description, and help text are defined on the **Documentation** pane. For this sample masked block, the pane looks like this.

Creating the Block Icon

So far, we have created a customized dialog box for the mx + b subsystem. However, the Subsystem block still displays the generic Simulink subsystem icon. An appropriate icon for this masked block is a plot that indicates the slope of the line. For a slope of 3, that icon looks like this.

The block icon is defined on the **Icon** pane. For this block, the **Icon** pane looks like this.

The drawing command plots a line from (0,0) to (1,m). If the slope is negative, Simulink shifts the line up by 1 to keep it within the visible drawing area of the block.

The drawing commands have access to all the variables in the mask workspace. As you enter different values of slope, the icon updates the slope of the plotted line.

Select **Normalized** as the **Drawing coordinates** parameter, located at the bottom of the list of icon properties, to specify that the icon be drawn in a frame whose bottom left corner is (0,0) and whose top right corner is (1,1). See "The Icon Pane" on page 10-14 for more information.

Masking a Subsystem

To mask a subsystem,

1 Select the subsystem.

2 Select **Edit mask** from the **Edit** menu of the model window or from the block's context menu. (Right-click the subsystem block to display its context menu.)

The Mask Editor appears.

See "The Mask Editor" on page 10-12 for a detailed description of the Mask Editor.

3 Use the Mask Editor's tabbed panes to perform any of the following tasks.

- Create a custom icon for the masked subsystem (see "The Icon Pane" on page 10-14)

- Create parameters that allow a user to set subsystem options (see "The Mask Editor" on page 10-12)

- Initialize the masked subsystem's parameters
- Create online user documentation for the subsystem

4 Click **Apply** to apply the mask to the subsystem or **OK** to apply the mask and dismiss the Mask Editor.

The Mask Editor

The Mask Editor allows you to create or edit a subsystem's mask. To open the Mask Editor, select the subsystem's block icon and then select **Edit Mask** from the **Edit** menu of the model window containing the subsystem's block. The Mask Editor appears.

The Mask Editor contains a set of tabbed panes, each of which enables you to define a feature of the mask:

- The **Icon** pane enables you to define the block icon (see "The Icon Pane" on page 10-14).
- The **Parameters** pane enables you to define and describe mask dialog box parameter prompts and name the variables associated with the parameters (see "The Parameters Pane" on page 10-17).
- The **Initialization** pane enables you to specify initialization commands (see "The Initialization Pane" on page 10-23).
- The **Documentation** pane enables you to define the mask type and specify the block description and the block help (see "The Documentation Pane" on page 10-25).

Five buttons appear along the bottom of the Mask Editor:

- The **Unmask** button deactivates the mask and closes the Mask Editor. The mask information is retained so that the mask can be reactivated. To reactivate the mask, select the block and choose **Create Mask**. The Mask Editor opens, displaying the previous settings. The inactive mask information is discarded when the model is closed and cannot be recovered.

- The **OK** button applies the mask settings on all panes and closes the Mask Editor.

- The **Cancel** button closes the Mask Editor without applying any changes made since you last clicked the **Apply** button.

- The **Help** button displays the contents of this chapter.

- The **Apply** button creates or changes the mask using the information that appears on all masking panes. The Mask Editor remains open.

To see the system under the mask without unmasking it, select the Subsystem block, then choose **Look Under Mask** from the **Edit** menu. This command opens the subsystem. The block's mask is not affected.

The Icon Pane

The Mask Editor's **Icon** pane enables you to create icons that can contain descriptive text, state equations, images, and graphics.

The **Icon** pane contains the following controls.

Drawing commands

This field allows you to enter commands that draw the block's icon. Simulink provides a set of commands that can display text, one or more plots, or show a transfer function (see "Mask Icon Drawing Commands") in the online Simulink reference). You must use these commands to draw your icon. Simulink executes the drawing commands in the order in which they appear in this field. Drawing commands have access to all variables in the mask workspace.

This example demonstrates how to create an improved icon for the mx + b sample masked subsystem discussed earlier in this chapter.

```
pos = get_param(gcb, 'Position');
width = pos(3) - pos(1); height = pos(4) - pos(2);
x = [0, width];
if (m >= 0), y = [0, (m*width)]; end
```

```
if (m < 0), y = [height, (height + (m*width))]; end
```

These initialization commands define the data that enables the drawing command to produce an accurate icon regardless of the shape of the block. The drawing command that generates this icon is plot(x,y).

Examples of drawing commands

This panel illustrates the usage of the various icon drawing commands supported by Simulink. To determine the syntax of a command, select the command from the **Command** list. Simulink displays an example of the selected command at the bottom of the panel and the icon produced by the command to the right of the list.

Icon options

These controls allow you to specify the following attributes of the block icon.

Frame. The icon frame is the rectangle that encloses the block. You can choose to show or hide the frame by setting the **Frame** parameter to Visible or Invisible. The default is to make the icon frame visible. For example, this figure shows visible and invisible icon frames for an AND gate block.

Visible   Invisible

Transparency. The icon can be set to Opaque or Transparent, either hiding or showing what is underneath the icon. Opaque, the default, covers information Simulink draws, such as port labels. This figure shows opaque and transparent icons for an AND gate block. Notice the text on the transparent icon.

Opaque   Transparent

Rotation. When the block is rotated or flipped, you can choose whether to rotate or flip the icon or to have it remain fixed in its original orientation. The default is not to rotate the icon. The icon rotation is consistent with block port rotation. This figure shows the results of choosing Fixed and Rotates icon rotation when the AND gate block is rotated.

Fixed   Rotates

Units. This option controls the coordinate system used by the drawing commands. It applies only to `plot` and `text` drawing commands. You can select from among these choices: `Autoscale`, `Normalized`, and `Pixel`.

Autoscale   Normalized   Pixel

- `Autoscale` scales the icon to fit the block frame. When the block is resized, the icon is also resized. For example, this figure shows the icon drawn using these vectors:

  X = [0 2 3 4 9]; Y = [4 6 3 5 8];

  The lower left corner of the block frame is (0,3) and the upper right corner is (9,8). The range of the *x*-axis is 9 (from 0 to 9), while the range of the *y*-axis is 5 (from 3 to 8).

- `Normalized` draws the icon within a block frame whose bottom left corner is (0,0) and whose top right corner is (1,1). Only X and Y values between 0 and 1 appear. When the block is resized, the icon is also resized. For example, this figure shows the icon drawn using these vectors:

  X = [.0 .2 .3 .4 .9]; Y = [.4 .6 .3 .5 .8];

- Pixel draws the icon with X and Y values expressed in pixels. The icon is not automatically resized when the block is resized. To force the icon to resize with the block, define the drawing commands in terms of the block size.

The Parameters Pane

The **Parameters** pane allows you to create and modify masked subsystem parameters (mask parameters, for short) that determine the behavior of the masked subsystem.

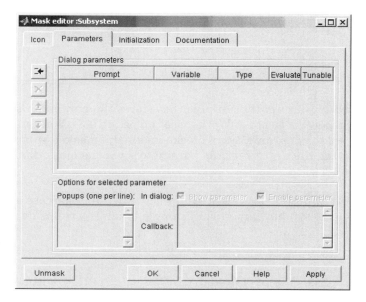

The **Parameters** pane contains the following elements:

- The **Dialog parameters** panel allows you to select and change the major properties of the mask's parameters (see "Dialog Parameters Panel" on page 10-18).
- The **Options for selected parameter** panel allows you to set additional options for the parameter selected in the **Dialog parameters** panel.
- The buttons on the left side of the **Parameters** pane allow you to add, delete, and change the order of appearance of parameters on the mask's parameter dialog box (see "Dialog Parameters Panel" on page 10-18).

Dialog Parameters Panel

Lists the mask's parameters in tabular form. Each row displays the major attributes of one of the mask's parameters.

Prompt. Text that identifies the parameter on a masked subsystem's dialog box.

Variable. Name of the variable that stores the parameter's value in the mask's workspace (see "Mask Workspace" on page 10-3). You can use this variable as the value of parameters of blocks inside the masked subsystem, thereby allowing the user to set the parameters via the mask dialog box.

Note Simulink does not distinguish between uppercase and lowercase letters in mask variable names. For example, Simulink treats gain, GAIN, and Gain as the same name.

Type. Type of control used to edit the value of this parameter. The control appears on the mask's parameter dialog box following the parameter prompt. The button that follows the type name in the **Parameters** pane pops up a list of the controls supported by Simulink (see "Control Types" on page 10-20). To change the current control type, select another type from the list.

Evaluate. If checked, this option causes Simulink to evaluates the expression entered by the user before it is assigned to the variable. Otherwise Simulink treats the expression itself as a string value and assigns it to the variable. For example, if the user enters the expression gain in an edit field and the **Evaluate** option is checked, Simulink evaluates gain and assigns the result to the variable. Otherwise, Simulink assigns the string 'gain' to the variable.

See "Check Box Control" on page 10-21 and "Pop-Up Control" on page 10-22 for information on how this option affects evaluation of the parameters.

If you need both the string entered and the evaluated value, uncheck the **Evaluate** option. Then use the MATLAB `eval` command in the initialization commands. For example, if `LitVal` is the string `'gain'`, then to obtain the evaluated value, use the command

```
value = eval(LitVal)
```

Tunable. Selecting this option allows a user to change the value of the mask parameter while a simulation is running.

Options for Selected Parameter Panel

This panel allows you to set additional options for the parameter selected in the **Dialog parameters** table.

Show parameter. The selected parameter appears on the masked block's parameter dialog box only if this option is checked (the default).

Enable parameter. Unchecking this option grays the selected parameter's prompt and disables its edit control. This means that the user cannot set the value of the parameter.

Popups. This field is enabled only if the edit control for the selected parameter is a pop-up. Enter the values of the pop-up control in this field, each on a separate line.

Callback. Enter MATLAB code that you want Simulink to execute when a user edits the selected parameter. The callback can create and reference variables only in the block's base workspace. If the callback needs the value of a mask parameter, it can use `get_param` to obtain the value, e.g.,

```
if str2num(get_param(gcb, 'g'))<0
    error('Gain is negative.')
end
```

Parameter Buttons

The following sections explain the purpose of the buttons that appear on the **Parameters** pane in the order of their appearance from the top of the pane.

Add Button. Adds a parameter to the mask's parameter list. The newly created parameter appears in the adjacent **Dialog parameters** table.

Delete Button. Deletes the parameter currently selected in the **Dialog parameters** table.

Up Button. Moves the currently selected parameter up one row in the **Dialog parameters** table. Dialog parameters appear in the mask's parameter dialog box (see "Mask Parameter Dialog Box" on page 10-3) in the same order in which they appear in the **Dialog parameters** table. This button (and the next) thus allows you to determine the order in which parameters appear on the dialog box.

Down Button. Moves the currently selected parameter down one row in the **Dialog parameters** table and hence down one position on the mask's parameter dialog box.

Control Types

Simulink enables you to choose how parameter values are entered or selected. You can create three styles of controls: edit fields, check boxes, and pop-up controls. For example, this figure shows the parameter area of a mask dialog box that uses all three styles of controls (with the pop-up control open).

Edit Control

An *edit field* enables the user to enter a parameter value by typing it into a field. This figure shows how the prompt for the sample edit control was defined.

The value of the variable associated with the parameter is determined by the **Evaluate** option.

Evaluate	Value
On	The result of evaluating the expression entered in the field
Off	The actual string entered in the field

Check Box Control

A *check box* enables the user to choose between two alternatives by selecting or deselecting a check box. This figure shows how the sample check box control is defined.

The value of the variable associated with the parameter depends on whether the **Evaluate** option is selected.

Control State	Evaluated Value	Literal Value
Checked	1	'on'
Unchecked	0	'off'

Pop-Up Control

A *pop-up* enables the user to choose a parameter value from a list of possible values. Specify the values in the **Popups** field on the **Parameters** pane (see "Popups" on page 10-19). The following example shows a pop-up parameter.

The value of the variable associated with the parameter (Color) depends on the item selected from the pop-up list and whether the **Evaluate** option is checked (on).

Evaluate	Value
On	Index of the value selected from the list, starting with 1. For example, if the third item is selected, the parameter value is 3.
Off	String that is the value selected. If the third item is selected, the parameter value is 'green'.

Changing Default Values for Mask Parameters in a Library

To change default parameter values in a masked library block, follow these steps:

1 Unlock the library.

2 Open the block to access its dialog box, fill in the desired default values, and close the dialog box.

3 Save the library.

When the block is copied into a model and opened, the default values appear on the block's dialog box.

For more information, see "Working with Block Libraries" on page 6-25.

The Initialization Pane

The **Initialization** pane allows you to enter MATLAB commands that initialize the masked subsystem.

Simulink executes the initialization commands when it

- Loads the model
- Starts the simulation or updates the block diagram
- Rotates the masked block
- Redraws the block's icon (if the mask's icon creation code depends on variables defined in the initialization code)

The **Initialization** pane includes the following controls.

Dialog variables

The **Dialog variables** list displays the names of the variables associated with the subsystem's mask parameters, i.e., the parameters defined in the **Parameters** pane. You can copy the name of a parameter from this list and paste it into the adjacent **Initialization commands** field, using the Simulink keyboard copy and paste commands. You can also use the list to change the names of mask parameter variables. To change a name, double-click the name in the list. An edit field containing the existing name appears. Edit existing name and press **Enter** or click outside the edit field to confirm your changes.

Initialization commands

Enter the initialization commands in this field. You can enter any valid MATLAB expression, consisting of MATLAB functions, operators, and variables defined in the mask workspace. Initialization commands cannot access base workspace variables. Terminate initialization commands with a semicolon to avoid echoing results to the Command Window.

Allow library block to modify its contents

This check box is enabled only if the masked subsystem resides in a library. Checking this block allows the block's initialization code to modify the contents of the masked subsystem, i.e., it lets the code add or delete blocks and set the parameters of those blocks. Otherwise, Simulink generates an error when a masked library block tries to modify its contents in any way. To set this option at the MATLAB prompt, select the self-modifying block and enter the following command.

```
set_param(gcb, 'MaskSelfModifiable', 'on');
```

Then save the block.

Debugging Initialization Commands

You can debug initialization commands in these ways:

- Specify an initialization command without a terminating semicolon to echo its results to the Command Window.
- Place a `keyboard` command in the initialization commands to stop execution and give control to the keyboard. For more information, see the help text for the `keyboard` command.
- Enter either of these commands in the MATLAB Command Window:

```
dbstop if error
```

```
dbstop if warning
```

If an error occurs in the initialization commands, execution stops and you can examine the mask workspace. For more information, see the help text for the dbstop command.

The Documentation Pane

The **Documentation** pane enables you to define or modify the type, description, and help text for a masked block. This figure shows how fields on the **Documentation** pane correspond to the mx + b sample mask block's dialog box.

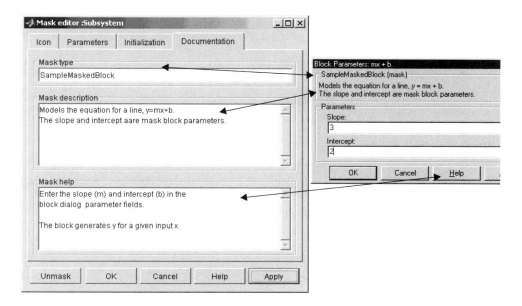

Mask Type Field

The mask type is a block classification used only for purposes of documentation. It appears in the block's dialog box and on all Mask Editor panes for the block. You can choose any name you want for the mask type. When Simulink creates the block's dialog box, it adds "(mask)" after the mask type to differentiate masked blocks from built-in blocks.

Mask Description Field

The block description is informative text that appears in the block's dialog box in the frame under the mask type. If you are designing a system for others to use, this is a good place to describe the block's purpose or function.

Simulink automatically wraps long lines of text. You can force line breaks by using the **Enter** or **Return** key.

Block Help Field

You can provide help text that is displayed when the **Help** button is clicked on the masked block's dialog box. If you create models for others to use, this is a good place to explain how the block works and how to enter its parameters.

You can include user-written documentation for a masked block's help. You can specify any of the following for the masked block help text:

- URL specification (a string starting with `http:`, `www`, `file:`, `ftp:`, or `mailto:`)
- `web` command (launches a browser)
- `eval` command (evaluates a MATLAB string)
- Static text displayed in the Web browser

Simulink examines the first line of the masked block help text. If it detects a URL specification, `web` command, or `eval` command, it accesses the block help as directed; otherwise, the full contents of the masked block help text are displayed in the browser.

These examples illustrate several acceptable commands:

```
web([docroot '/My Blockset Doc/' get_param(gcb,'MaskType')...
'.html'])

eval('!Word My_Spec.doc')

http://www.mathworks.com

file:///c:/mydir/helpdoc.html

www.mathworks.com
```

Simulink automatically wraps long lines of text.

Linking Mask Parameters to Block Parameters

The variables associated with mask parameters allow you to link mask parameters with block parameters. This in turn allows a user to use the mask to set the values of parameters of blocks inside the masked subsystem.

To link the parameters, open the block's parameter dialog box and enter an expression in the block parameter's value field that uses the mask parameter. The mx + b masked subsystem, described earlier in this chapter, uses this approach to link the Slope and Intercept mask parameters to corresponding parameters of a Gain and Constant block, respectively, that reside in the subsystem.

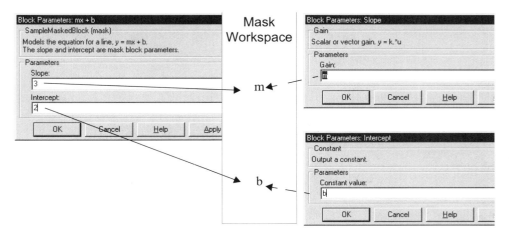

You can use a masked block's initialization code to link mask parameters indirectly to block parameters. In this approach, the initialization code creates variables in the mask workspace whose values are functions of the mask parameters and that appear in expressions that set the values of parameters of blocks concealed by the mask.

Simulink Debugger

The following sections tell you how to use the Simulink debugger to pinpoint bugs in a model.

Introduction (p. 11-2) — Overview of the debugger.

Starting the Debugger (p. 11-3) — How to start the debugger.

Starting the Simulation (p. 11-4) — How to start a simulation from the debugger.

Using the Debugger's Command-Line Interface (p. 11-6) — How to debug from the MATLAB command line.

Getting Online Help (p. 11-7) — How to get help on debugger commands.

Running a Simulation (p. 11-8) — How to start, step, and stop a simulation in debug mode.

Setting Breakpoints (p. 11-12) — How to set breakpoints at blocks and time steps.

Displaying Information About the Simulation (p. 11-17) — How to display information about the current simulation.

Displaying Information About the Model (p. 11-21) — How to display information about the model being debugged.

Introduction

The Simulink debugger is a tool for locating and diagnosing bugs in a Simulink model. It enables you to pinpoint problems by running simulations step by step and displaying intermediate block states and input and outputs. The Simulink debugger has both a graphical and a command-line user interface. The graphical interface allows you to access the debugger's most commonly used features. The command-line interface gives you access to all the debugger's capabilities. Wherever you can use either interface to perform a task, the documentation shows you first how to use the graphical interface and then the command-line interface to perform the task.

Starting the Debugger

To start the debugger, open the model you want to debug and select **Debugger** from the Simulink **Tools** menu. The debugger window appears.

You can also start the debugger from the MATLAB command line, using the `sldebug` command or the `debug` option of the `sim` command to start a model under debugger control. For example, either the command

```
sim('vdp',[0,10],simset('debug','on'))
```

or the command

```
sldebug 'vdp'
```

loads the Simulink demo model vdp into memory, starts the simulation, and stops the simulation at the first block in the model's execution list.

Note When running the debugger in graphical user interface (GUI) mode, you must explicitly start the simulation. See "Starting the Simulation" on page 11-4 for more information.

Starting the Simulation

To start the simulation, select the Start/Continue button in the debugger's toolbar.

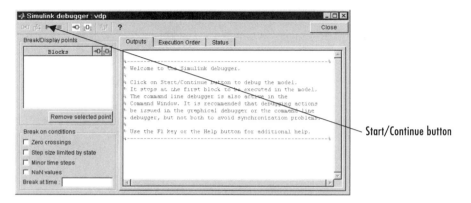

Start/Continue button

The simulation starts and stops at the first block to be executed. The debugger opens the model window's browser pane and highlights the block at which model execution has stopped.

First block to be executed

The debugger displays the simulation start time and a debug command prompt in the MATLAB Command Window when the debugger is running in command-line mode or in the debugger's output pane when the debugger is running in GUI mode.

The command prompt displays the block index (see "Block Indexes" on page 11-6) and the name of the first block to be executed.

Note When you start the debugger in GUI mode, the debugger's command-line interface is also active in the MATLAB Command Window. However, you should avoid using the command-line interface, to prevent synchronization errors between the graphical and command-line interfaces.

At this point, you can set breakpoints, run the simulation step by step, continue the simulation to the next breakpoint or end, examine data, or perform other debugging tasks. The following sections explain how to use the debugger's graphical controls to perform these debugging tasks.

Using the Debugger's Command-Line Interface

In command line mode, you control the debugger by entering commands at the debugger command line in the MATLAB Command Window. The debugger accepts abbreviations for debugger commands. See "Debugger Command Reference" in the online Simulink Help for a list of command abbreviations and repeatable commands. You can repeat some commands by entering an empty command (i.e., by pressing the **Return** key) at the MATLAB command line.

Block Indexes

Many Simulink debugger commands and messages use block indexes to refer to blocks. A block index has the form s:b where s is an integer identifying a system in the model being debugged and b is an integer identifying a block within that system. For example, the block index 0:1 refers to block 1 in the model's 0 system. The slist command shows the block index for each block in the model being debuggedslist in the "Debugger Command Reference" in the online Simulink Help.

Accessing the MATLAB Workspace

You can enter any MATLAB expression at the sldebug prompt. For example, suppose you are at a breakpoint and you are logging time and output of your model as tout and yout. Then the following command

```
(sldebug ...) plot(tout, yout)
```

creates a plot. Suppose you would like to access a variable whose name is the same as the complete or incomplete name of an sldebug command, for example, s, which is a partial completion for the step command. Typing an s at the sldebug prompt steps the model. However,

```
(sldebug...) eval('s')
```

displays the value of the variable s.

Getting Online Help

You can get online help on using the debugger by clicking the Help button on the debugger's toolbar or by pressing the **F1** key when the text cursor is in a debugger panel or text field. Clicking the Help button displays help for the debugger in the MATLAB Help browser.

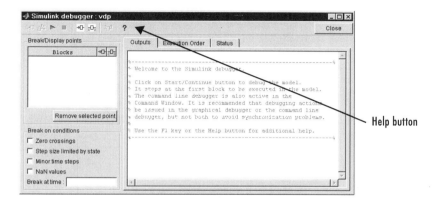

Help button

Pressing the **F1** key displays help for the debugger panel or text field that currently has the keyboard input focus. In command-line mode, you can get a brief description of the debugger commands by typing help at the debug prompt.

Running a Simulation

The Simulink debugger lets you run a simulation from the point at which it is currently suspended to the following points:

- End of the simulation
- Next breakpoint (see "Setting Breakpoints" on page 11-12)
- Next block
- Next time step

You select the amount to advance by selecting the appropriate button on the debugger toolbar in GUI mode

or by entering the appropriate debugger command in command-line mode.

Command	Advances a Simulation
step	One block
next	One time step
continue	To next breakpoint
run	To end of simulation, ignoring breakpoints

Continuing a Simulation

In GUI mode, the debugger colors the Stop button red when it has suspended the simulation for any reason. To continue the simulation, click the Start/Continue button. In command-line mode, enter continue to continue the simulation. The debugger continues the simulation to the next breakpoint (see

"Setting Breakpoints" on page 11-12) or to the end of the simulation, whichever comes first.

Running a Simulation Nonstop

The run command lets you run a simulation from the current point in the simulation to the end, skipping any intervening breakpoints. At the end of the simulation, the debugger returns you to the MATLAB command line. To continue debugging a model, you must restart the debugger.

Note The GUI mode does not provide a graphical version of the run command. To run the simulation to the end, you must first clear all breakpoints and then click the Continue button.

Advancing to the Next Block

To advance a simulation one block, click ▣▶▣ on the debugger toolbar or, if the debugger is running in command-line mode, enter step at the debugger prompt. The debugger executes the current block, stops, and highlights the next block in the model's block execution order (see "Displaying a Model's Block Execution Order" on page 11-21). For example, the following figure shows the vdp block diagram after execution of the model's first block.

If the next block to be executed occurs in a subsystem block, the debugger opens the subsystem's block diagram and highlights the next block.

After executing a block, the debugger prints the block's inputs (U) and outputs (Y) and redisplays the debug command prompt in the debugger output panel (in GUI mode) or in the MATLAB Command Window (in command-line mode).

The debugger prompt shows the next block to be evaluated.

```
(sldebug @0:0 'vdp/Integrator1'): step
U1 = [0]
CSTATE = [2]
Y1 = [2]
(sldebug @0:1 'vdp/Out1'):
```

Crossing a Time Step Boundary

After executing the last block in the model's block execution list, the debugger advances the simulation to the next time step and halts the simulation. To signal that you have crossed a time step boundary, the debugger prints the current time in the debugger output panel in GUI mode or in the MATLAB Command Window in command-line mode. For example, stepping through the last block of the first time step of the vdp model results in the following output in the debugger output panel or the MATLAB Command Window.

```
(sldebug @0:8 'vdp/Sum'): step
 U1 = [2]
 U2 = [0]
 Y1 = [-2]
[Tm=0.0001004754572603832  ] **Start** of system 'vdp' outputs
```

Stepping by Minor Time Steps

You can step by blocks within minor time steps as well as within major steps. To step by blocks within minor time steps, select the **Minor time steps** option on the debugger's **Break on conditions** panel or enter minor at the debugger command prompt.

Advancing to the Next Time Step

To advance to the next time step, click ⊞ or enter the next command at the debugger command line. The debugger executes the remaining blocks in the current time step and advances the simulation to the beginning of the next time step. For example, entering next after starting the vdp model in debug mode causes the following message to appear in the MATLAB Command Window.

```
[Tm=0.0001004754572603832  ] **Start** of system 'vdp' outputs
```

Setting Breakpoints

The Simulink debugger allows you to define stopping points in a simulation called breakpoints. You can then run a simulation from breakpoint to breakpoint, using the debugger's continue command. The debugger lets you define two types of breakpoints: unconditional and conditional. An unconditional breakpoint occurs whenever a simulation reaches a block or time step that you specified previously. A conditional breakpoint occurs when a condition that you specified in advance arises in the simulation.

Breakpoints come in handy when you know that a problem occurs at a certain point in your program or when a certain condition occurs. By defining an appropriate breakpoint and running the simulation via the continue command, you can skip immediately to the point in the simulation where the problem occurs.

You set a breakpoint by clicking the breakpoint button on the debugger toolbar

or by selecting the appropriate breakpoint conditions (GUI mode)

or by entering the appropriate breakpoint command (command-line mode).

Command	Causes Simulation to Stop
break <gcb | s:b>	At the beginning of a block
bafter <gcb | s:b>	At the end of a block

Command	Causes Simulation to Stop
tbreak [t]	At a simulation time step
nanbreak	At the occurrence of an underflow or overflow (NaN) or infinite (Inf) value
xbreak	When the simulation reaches the state that determines the simulation step size
zcbreak	When a zero crossing occurs between simulation time steps

Setting Breakpoints at Blocks

The debugger lets you specify a breakpoint at the beginning of the execution of a block or at the end of the execution of a block (command-line mode only).

Specifying a Breakpoint at the Start of a Block's Execution

Setting a breakpoint at the beginning of a block causes the debugger to stop the simulation when it reaches the block on each time step. You can specify the block on which to set the breakpoint graphically or via a block index in command-line mode. To set a breakpoint graphically at the beginning of a block's execution, select the block in the model window and click ⬚ on the debugger's toolbar or enter

```
break gcb
```

at the debugger command line. To specify the block via its block index (command-line mode only), enter

```
break s:b
```

where s:b is the block's index (see "Block Indexes" on page 11-6).

Note You cannot set a breakpoint on a virtual block. A virtual block is a block whose function is purely graphical: it indicates a grouping or relationship among a model's computational blocks. The debugger warns you if you attempt to set a breakpoint on a virtual block. You can obtain a listing of a model's nonvirtual blocks, using the slist command (see "Displaying a Model's Nonvirtual Blocks" on page 11-22).

In GUI mode, the debugger's **Break/Display points** panel displays the blocks where breakpoints exist.

Setting a Breakpoint at the End of a Block's Execution

In command-line mode, the debugger allows you to set a breakpoint at the end of a block's execution, using the bafter command. As with break, you can specify the block graphically or via its block index.

Clearing Breakpoints from Blocks

To clear a breakpoint temporarily, clear the first check box next to the breakpoint in the **Break/Display points** panel (GUI mode only). To clear a breakpoint permanently in GUI mode, select the breakpoint in the **Break/Display points** panel and click the **Remove selected point** button. In command-line mode use the clear command to clear breakpoints. You can specify the block by entering its block index or by selecting the block in the model diagram and entering gcb as the argument of the clear command.

Setting Breakpoints at Time Steps

To set a breakpoint at a time step, enter a time in the debugger's **Break at time** field (GUI mode) or enter the time using the tbreak command. This causes the debugger to stop the simulation at the beginning of the first time step that follows the specified time. For example, starting vdp in debug mode and entering the commands

```
tbreak 9
continue
```

causes the debugger to halt the simulation at the beginning of time step 9.0785 as indicated by the output of the continue command.

```
[Tm=9.07847133212036        ] **Start** of system 'vdp' outputs
```

Breaking on Nonfinite Values

Selecting the debugger's **NaN values** option or entering the nanbreak command causes the simulation to stop when a computed value is infinite or outside the range of values that can be represented by the machine running the simulation. This option is useful for pinpointing computational errors in a Simulink model.

Breaking on Step-Size Limiting Steps

Selecting the **Step size limited by state** option or entering the xbreak command causes the debugger to stop the simulation when the model uses a variable-step solver and the solver encounters a state that limits the size of the steps that it can take. This command is useful in debugging models that appear to require an excessive number of simulation time steps to solve.

Breaking at Zero Crossings

Selecting the **Zero crossings** option or entering the zcbreak command causes the simulation to halt when Simulink detects a nonsampled zero crossing in a model that includes blocks where zero crossings can arise. After halting, Simulink displays the location in the model, the time, and the type (rising or falling) of the zero crossing. For example, setting a zero-crossing break at the start of execution of the zeroxing demo model,

```
sldebug zeroxing
[Tm=0                   ] **Start** of system 'zeroxing' outputs
(sldebug @0:0 'zeroxing/Sine Wave'): zcbreak
Break at zero crossing events is enabled.
```

and continuing the simulation

```
(sldebug @0:0 'zeroxing/Sine Wave'): continue
```

results in a rising zero-crossing break at

```
[Tm=0.34350110879329        ] Breaking at block 0:2

[Tm=0.34350110879329        ] Rising zero crossing on 3rd zcsignal
in block 0:2 'zeroxing/Saturation'
```

If a model does not include blocks capable of producing nonsampled zero crossings, the command prints a message advising you of this fact.

Displaying Information About the Simulation

The Simulink debugger provides a set of commands that allow you to display block states, block inputs and outputs, and other information while running a model.

Displaying Block I/O

The debugger allows you to display block I/O by selecting the appropriate buttons on the debugger toolbar

Watch Block I/O   Display Block I/O

or by entering the appropriate debugger command.

Command	Displays a Block's I/O
probe	Immediately
disp	At every breakpoint
trace	Whenever the block executes

11-17

Displaying I/O of Selected Block

To display the I/O of a block, select the block and click ⊡ in GUI mode or enter the probe command in command-line mode.

Command	Description
probe	Enter or exit probe mode. In probe mode, the debugger displays the current inputs and outputs of any block that you select in the model's block diagram. Typing any command causes the debugger to exit probe mode.
probe gcb	Display I/O of selected block.
probe s:b	Print the I/O of the block specified by system number s and block number b.

The debugger prints the current inputs, outputs, and states of the selected block in the debugger output pane (GUI mode) or the MATLAB Command Window.

The probe command comes in handy when you need to examine the I/O of a block whose I/O is not otherwise displayed. For example, suppose you are using the step command to run a model block by block. Each time you step the model, the debugger displays the inputs and outputs of the current block. The probe command lets you examine the I/O of other blocks as well. Similarly, suppose you are using the next command to step through a model by time steps. The next command does not display block I/O. However, if you need to examine a block's I/O after entering a next command, you can do so using the probe command.

Displaying Block I/O Automatically at Breakpoints

The disp command causes the debugger to display a specified block's inputs and outputs whenever it halts the simulation. You can specify a block either by entering its block index or by selecting it in the block diagram and entering gcb as the disp command argument. You can remove any block from the debugger's list of display points, using the undisp command. For example, to remove block 0:0, either select the block in the model diagram and enter undisp gcb or simply enter undisp 0:0.

Note Automatic display of block I/O at breakpoints is not available in the debugger's GUI mode.

The disp command is useful when you need to monitor the I/O of a specific block or set of blocks as you step through a simulation. Using the disp command, you can specify the blocks you want to monitor and the debugger will then redisplay the I/O of those blocks on every step. Note that the debugger always displays the I/O of the current block when you step through a model block by block, using the step command. So, you do not need to use the disp command if you are interested in watching only the I/O of the current block.

Watching Block I/O

To watch a block, select the block and click ⊒▫▤ in the debugger toolbar or enter the trace command. In GUI mode, if a breakpoint exists on the block, you can set a watch on it as well by selecting the watch check box for the block in the **Break/Display points** pane. In command-line mode, you can also specify the block by specifying its block index in the trace command. You can remove a block from the debugger's list of trace points, using the untrace command.

The debugger displays a watched block's I/O whenever the block executes. Watching a block allows you obtain a complete record of the block's I/O without having to stop the simulation.

Displaying Algebraic Loop Information

The atrace command causes the debugger to display information about a model's algebraic loops (see "Algebraic Loops" on page 3-18) each time they are solved. The command takes a single argument that specifies the amount of information to display.

Command	Displays for Each Algebraic Loop
atrace 0	No information
atrace 1	The loop variable solution, the number of iterations required to solve the loop, and the estimated solution error
atrace 2	Same as level 1

Command	Displays for Each Algebraic Loop
atrace 3	Level 2 plus the Jacobian matrix used to solve the loop
atrace 4	Level 3 plus intermediate solutions of the loop variable

Displaying System States

The states debug command lists the current values of the system's states in the MATLAB Command Window. For example, the following sequence of commands shows the states of the Simulink bouncing ball demo (bounce) after its first and second time steps.

```
sldebug bounce
[Tm=0                        ] **Start** of system 'bounce' outputs
(sldebug @0:0 'bounce/Position'): states
Continuous state vector (value,index,name):
   10                        0 (0:0 'bounce/Position')
   15                        1 (0:5 'bounce/Velocity')
(sldebug @0:0 'bounce/Position'): next
[Tm=0.01                     ] **Start** of system 'bounce' outputs
(sldebug @0:0 'bounce/Position'): states
Continuous state vector (value,index,name):
   10.1495095                0 (0:0 'bounce/Position')
   14.9019                   1 (0:5 'bounce/Velocity')
```

Displaying Integration Information

The ishow command toggles display of integration information. When enabled, this option causes the debugger to display a message each time the simulation takes a time step or encounters a state that limits the size of a time step. In the first case, the debugger displays the size of the time step, for example,

```
[Tm=9.996264188473381       ] Step of 0.01 was taken by integrator
```

In the second case, the debugger displays the state that currently determines the size of time steps, for example,

```
[Ts=9.676264188473388       ] Integration limited by 1st state of
block 0:0 'bounce/Position'
```

Displaying Information About the Model

In addition to providing information about a simulation, the debugger can provide you with information about the model that underlies the simulation.

Displaying a Model's Block Execution Order

Simulink determines the order in which to execute blocks at the beginning of a simulation run, during model initialization. During simulation, Simulink maintains a list of blocks sorted by execution order. This list is called the sorted list. In GUI mode, the debugger displays the sorted list in its **Execution Order** panel. In command-line mode, the slist command displays the model's block execution order in the MATLAB Command Window. The list includes the block index for each command.

```
---- Sorted list for 'vdp' [12 blocks, 9 nonvirtual blocks,
directFeed=0]
    0:0     'vdp/Integrator1' (Integrator)
    0:1     'vdp/Out1' (Outport)
    0:2     'vdp/Integrator2' (Integrator)
    0:3     'vdp/Out2' (Outport)
    0:4     'vdp/Fcn' (Fcn)
    0:5     'vdp/Product' (Product)
    0:6     'vdp/Mu' (Gain)
    0:7     'vdp/Scope' (Scope)
    0:8     'vdp/Sum' (Sum)
```

Identifying Blocks in Algebraic Loops

If a block belongs to an algebraic list, the slist command displays an algebraic loop identifier in the entry for the block in the sorted list. The identifier has the form

```
algId=s#n
```

where s is the index of the subsystem containing the algebraic loop and n is the index of the algebraic loop in the subsystem. For example, the following entry for an Integrator block indicates that it participates in the first algebraic loop at the root level of the model.

```
0:1 'test/ss/I1' (Integrator, tid=0) [algId=0#1, discontinuity]
```

You can use the debugger's ashow command to highlight the blocks and lines that make up an algebraic loop. See "Displaying Algebraic Loops" on page 11-24 for more information.

Displaying a Block

To determine the block in a model's diagram that corresponds to a particular index, enter bshow s:b at the command prompt, where s:b is the block index. The bshow command opens the system containing the block (if necessary) and selects the block in the system's window.

Displaying a Model's Nonvirtual Systems

The systems command displays a list of the nonvirtual systems in the model being debugged. For example, the Simulink clutch demo (clutch) contains the following systems:

```
sldebug clutch
[Tm=0                          ] **Start** of system 'clutch' outputs
(sldebug @0:0 'clutch/Clutch Pedal'): systems
  0    'clutch'
  1    'clutch/Locked'
  2    'clutch/Unlocked'
```

Note The systems command does not list subsystems that are purely graphical in nature, that is, subsystems that the model diagram represents as Subsystem blocks but that Simulink solves as part of a parent system. In Simulink models, the root system and triggered or enabled subsystems are true systems. All other subsystems are virtual (that is, graphical) and hence do not appear in the listing produced by the systems command.

Displaying a Model's Nonvirtual Blocks

The slist command displays a list of the nonvirtual blocks in a model. The listing groups the blocks by system. For example, the following sequence of commands produces a list of the nonvirtual blocks in the Van der Pol (vdp) demo model.

```
sldebug vdp
[Tm=0                          ] **Start** of system 'vdp' outputs
```

```
(sldebug @0:0 'vdp/Integrator1'): slist
---- Sorted list for 'vdp' [12 blocks, 9 nonvirtual blocks,
directFeed=0]
  0:0    'vdp/Integrator1' (Integrator)
  0:1    'vdp/Out1' (Outport)
  0:2    'vdp/Integrator2' (Integrator)
  0:3    'vdp/Out2' (Outport)
  0:4    'vdp/Fcn' (Fcn)
  0:5    'vdp/Product' (Product)
  0:6    'vdp/Mu' (Gain)
  0:7    'vdp/Scope' (Scope)
  0:8    'vdp/Sum' (Sum)
```

Note The slist command does not list blocks that are purely graphical in nature, that is, blocks that indicate relationships or groupings among computational blocks.

Displaying Blocks with Potential Zero Crossings

The zclist command displays a list of blocks in which nonsampled zero crossings can occur during a simulation. For example, zclist displays the following list for the clutch sample model:

```
(sldebug @0:0 'clutch/Clutch Pedal'): zclist
  2:3    'clutch/Unlocked/Sign' (Signum)
  0:4    'clutch/Lockup Detection/Velocities Match' (HitCross)
  0:10   'clutch/Lockup Detection/Required Friction
           for Lockup/Abs' (Abs)
  0:11   'clutch/Lockup Detection/Required Friction for
           Lockup/ Relational Operator' (RelationalOperator)
  0:18   'clutch/Break Apart Detection/Abs' (Abs)
  0:20   'clutch/Break Apart Detection/Relational Operator'
           (RelationalOperator)
  0:24   'clutch/Unlocked' (SubSystem)
  0:27   'clutch/Locked' (SubSystem)
```

11-23

Displaying Algebraic Loops

The ashow command highlights a specified algebraic loop or the algebraic loop that contains a specified block. To highlight a specified algebraic loop, enter ashow s#n, where s is the index of the system (see "Identifying Blocks in Algebraic Loops" on page 11-21) that contains the loop and n is the index of the loop in the system. To display the loop that contains the currently selected block, enter ashow gcb. To show a loop that contains a specified block, enter ashow s:b, where s:b is the block's index. To clear algebraic-loop highlighting from the model diagram, enter ashow clear.

Displaying Debugger Status

In GUI mode, the debugger displays the settings of various debug options, such as conditional breakpoints, in its **Status** panel. In command-line mode, the status command displays debugger settings. For example, the following sequence of commands displays the initial debug settings for the vdp model:

```
sim('vdp',[0,10],simset('debug','on'))
[Tm=0                      ] **Start** of system 'vdp' outputs
(sldebug @0:0 'vdp/Integrator1'): status
  Current simulation time: 0 (MajorTimeStep)
  Last command: ""
  Stop in minor times steps is disabled.
  Break at zero crossing events is disabled.
  Break when step size is limiting by a state is disabled.
  Break on non-finite (NaN,Inf) values is disabled.
  Display of integration information is disabled.
  Algebraic loop tracing level is at 0.
```

Block Libraries

The following sections describe the usage and contents of the Simulink block libraries. You can use either the Simulink Library Browser on Windows or the MATLAB command `simulink` on UNIX to display and browse the libraries.

Continuous (p. A-2)	Blocks that model linear functions.
Discontinuities (p. A-3)	Blocks whose outputs are discontinuous functions of their inputs.
Discrete (p. A-4)	Blocks that represent discrete-time functions.
Look-Up Tables (p. A-5)	Blocks that use look-up tables to determine outputs from inputs.
Math Operations (p. A-6)	Blocks that model general mathematical functions.
Model Verification (p. A-8)	Blocks that enable you to create self-validating models.
Model-Wide Utilities (p. A-10)	Various utility blocks.
Ports & Subsystems (p. A-11)	Blocks for creating various types of subsystems.
Signal Attributes (p. A-13)	Blocks that modify or output attributes of signals.
Signal Routing (p. A-14)	Blocks that route signals from one point in a block diagram to another.
Sinks (p. A-15)	Blocks that display or write block output.
Sources (p. A-16)	Blocks that generate signals.
User-Defined Functions (p. A-18)	Blocks that allow you to define the function that relates inputs to outputs.
Blocksets and Toolboxes (p. A-19)	Extras block library of specialized blocks.
Demos Library (p. A-20)	MATLAB and Simulink demos.

Continuous

The *Continuous* library contains blocks that model linear functions.

Block Name	Purpose
Derivative	Output the time derivative of the input.
Integrator	Integrate a signal.
State-Space	Implement a linear state-space system.
Transfer Fcn	Implement a linear transfer function.
Transport Delay	Delay the input by a given amount of time.
Variable Transport Delay	Delay the input by a variable amount of time.
Zero-Pole	Implement a transfer function specified in terms of poles and zeros.

Discontinuities

The *Discontinuities* library contains blocks whose outputs are discontinuous functions of their inputs.

Block Name	Purpose
Backlash	Model the behavior of a system with play.
Coulomb and Viscous Friction	Model discontinuity at zero, with linear gain elsewhere.
Dead Zone	Provide a region of zero output.
Hit Crossing	Detect crossing point.
Quantizer	Discretize input at a specified interval.
Rate Limiter	Limit the rate of change of a signal.
Relay	Switch output between two constants.
Saturation	Limit the range of a signal.

Discrete

The *Discrete* library contains blocks that represent discrete-time functions.

Block Name	Purpose
Discrete Filter	Implement IIR and FIR filters.
Discrete State-Space	Implement a discrete state-space system.
Discrete Transfer Fcn	Implement a discrete transfer function.
Discrete Zero-Pole	Implement a discrete transfer function specified in terms of poles and zeros.
Discrete-Time Integrator	Perform discrete-time integration of a signal.
First-Order Hold	Implement a first-order sample-and-hold.
Memory	Output the block input from the previous time step.
Unit Delay	Delay a signal one sample period.
Zero-Order Hold	Implement zero-order hold of one sample period.

Look-Up Tables

The *Look-Up Tables* library contains blocks that use lookup tables to determine outputs from inputs.

Block Name	Purpose
Direct Look-Up Table (n-D)	Index into an N-dimensional table to retrieve a scalar, vector or 2-D matrix.
Interpolation (n-D) Using PreLook-Up	Perform high-performance constant or linear interpolation.
Look-Up Table	Perform piecewise linear mapping of the input.
Look-Up Table (2-D)	Perform piecewise linear mapping of two inputs.
Look-Up Table (n-D)	Perform piecewise linear or spline mapping of two or more inputs.
Prelook-Up Index Search	Perform index search and interval fraction calculation for input on a breakpoint set.

Math Operations

The *Math Operations* library contains blocks that model general mathematical functions.

Block Name	Purpose
Abs	Output the absolute value of the input.
Algebraic Constraint	Constrain the input signal to zero.
Assignment	Assign values to specified elements of a signal
Bitwise Logical Operator	Logically mask, invert, or shift the bits of an unsigned integer signal.
Combinatorial Logic	Implement a truth table.
Complex to Magnitude-Angle	Output the phase and magnitude of a complex input signal.
Complex to Real-Imag	Output the real and imaginary parts of a complex input signal.
Dot Product	Generate the dot product.
Gain, Matrix Gain	Multiply block input by a specified value.
Logical Operator	Perform the specified logical operation on the input.
Magnitude-Angle to Complex	Output a complex signal from magnitude and phase inputs.
Math Function	Perform a mathematical function.
Matrix Concatenation	Concatenate inputs horizontally or vertically
MinMax	Output the minimum or maximum input value.

Block Name	Purpose (Continued)
Polynomial	Perform evaluation of polynomial coefficients on input values.
Product	Generate the product or quotient of block inputs.
Real-Imag to Complex	Output a complex signal from real and imaginary inputs.
Relational Operator	Perform the specified relational operation on the input.
Reshape	Change the dimensionality of a signal.
Rounding Function	Perform a rounding function.
Sign	Indicate the sign of the input.
Slider Gain	Vary a scalar gain using a slider.
Sum	Generate the sum of inputs.
Trigonometric Function	Perform a trigonometric function.

Model Verification

Acknowledgment. The Model Verification blocks were developed in conjunction with the Control System Design team of the Advanced Chassis System Development group of DaimlerChrysler AG, Stuttgart, Germany.

The Model Verification library contains blocks that enable you to create self-validating models.

Block Name	Purpose
Assertion	Assert that the input signal is nonzero.
Check Discrete Gradient	Check that the absolute value of the difference between successive samples of a discrete signal is less than an upper bound.
Check Dynamic Gap	Check that a gap of varying width occurs in the range of a signal's amplitudes.
Check Dynamic Lower Bound	Check that a signal is always greater than a value that can vary at each time step.
Check Dynamic Range	Check that a signal always lies in a varying range of amplitudes.
Check Dynamic Upper Bound	Check that a signal is always less than a value that can vary at each time step.
Check Input Resolution	Check that a signal has a specified resolution.
Check Static Gap	Check that a fixed-width gap occurs in the range of a signal's amplitudes
Check Static Lower Bound	Check that a signal is greater than (or optionally equal to) a lower bound that does not vary with time.
Check Static Range	Check that the input signal falls in a fixed range of amplitudes.

Block Name	Purpose (Continued)
Check Static Upper Bound	Check that a signal is less than (or optionally equal to) an upper bound that does not vary with time.

Model-Wide Utilities

The *Model-Wide Utilities* library contains various utility blocks.

Block Name	Purpose
DocBlock	Create text that documents the model and save the text with the model.
Model Info	Display revision control information in a model.
Time-Based Linearization	Generate linear models in the base workspace at specific times.
Trigger-Based Linearization	Generate linear models in the base workspace when triggered.

Ports & Subsystems

The Ports & Subsystems library contains blocks for creating various types of subsystems.

Block Name	Purpose
Action Port	Repository for conditionally executed logic for If and Switch-Case blocks. Note: this block resides inside the If Action Subsystem and Switch-Case Action Subsystem blocks in the Subsystems library.
Configurable Subsystem	Represent any block selected from a specified library.
Enable	Add an enabling port to a subsystem. Note that this block resides inside the Enabled Subsystem and the Enabled and Triggered Subsystem in the Subsystems library.
Enabled and Triggered Subsystem	Skeleton enabled and triggered subsystem.
Enabled Subsystem	Skeleton enabled subsystem.
For Iterator	Implements C-like `for` statement logic.
For Iterator Subsystem	Implements a C-like `for` loop.
Function-Call Subsystem	Skeleton function call subsystem.
If	Implements C-like `if-else` statement logic.
Inport	Create an input port for a subsystem or an external input. Note that this block resides inside the Subsystem block and inside other subsystem blocks in the Subsystems library.

Block Name	Purpose (Continued)
Outport	Create an output port for a subsystem or an external output. Note that this block resides inside the Subsystem block and inside other subsystem blocks in the Subsystems library.
Subsystem, Atomic Subsystem	Represent a system within another system.
Switch Case	Implements C-like `switch` statement logic.
Switch Case Action Subsystem	Represent a subsystem whose execution is triggered by a Switch Case block.
Trigger	Add a trigger port to a subsystem. Note this block resides inside the Triggered Subsystem and the Enabled and Triggered Subsystem in the Subsystems library.
Triggered Subsystem	Skeleton triggered subsystem.
While Iterator	Implement a C-like `while` or `do-while` control flow statement as a While subsystem.
While Iterator Subsystem	Represent a subsystem that executes repeatedly while a condition is satisfied during a simulation time step.

Signal Attributes

The *Signal Attributes* library contains blocks that modify or output attributes of signals.

Block Name	Purpose
Data Type Conversion	Convert a signal to another data type.
IC	Set the initial value of a signal.
Rate Transition	Specify the data transfer mechanism between the data rates of a multirate system.
Probe	Output a signal's attributes, including width, sample time, and/or signal type.
Signal Specification	Specify attributes of a signal.
Width	Output the width of the input vector.

Signal Routing

The *Signal Routing* library contains blocks that route signals from one point in a block diagram to another.

Block Name	Purpose
Bus Creator	Create a signal bus.
Bus Selector	Output signals selected from an input bus.
Data Store Memory	Define a shared data store.
Data Store Read	Read data from a shared data store.
Data Store Write	Write data to a shared data store.
Demux	Separate a vector signal into output signals.
From	Accept input from a Goto block.
Goto	Pass block input to From blocks.
Goto Tag Visibility	Define the scope of a Goto block tag.
Manual Switch	Switch between two inputs.
Merge	Combine several input lines into a scalar line.
Multi-Port Switch	Choose between block inputs.
Mux	Combine several input lines into a vector line.
Selector	Select or reorder the elements of the input vector.
Switch	Switch between two inputs.

Sinks

The *Sinks* library contains blocks that display or write block output.

Block Name	Purpose
Display	Show the value of the input.
Outport	Create an output port for a subsystem or an external output.
Scope, Floating Scope	Display signals generated during a simulation.
Stop Simulation	Stop the simulation when the input is nonzero.
Terminator	Terminate an unconnected output port.
To File	Write data to a file.
To Workspace	Write data to a variable in the workspace.
XY Graph	Display an X-Y plot of signals using a MATLAB figure window.

Sources

The *Sources* library contains blocks that generate signals.

Block Name	Purpose
Band-Limited White Noise	Introduce white noise into a continuous system.
Chirp Signal	Generate a sine wave with increasing frequency.
Clock	Display and provide the simulation time.
Constant	Generate a constant value.
Digital Clock	Generate simulation time at the specified sampling interval.
From File	Read data from a file.
From Workspace	Read data from a variable defined in the workspace.
Ground	Ground an unconnected input port.
Inport	Create an input port for a subsystem or an external input.
Pulse Generator	Generate pulses at regular intervals.
Ramp	Generate a constantly increasing or decreasing signal.
Random Number	Generate normally distributed random numbers.
Repeating Sequence	Generate a repeatable arbitrary signal.
Signal Builder	Generate an arbitrary piecewise linear signal.
Signal Generator	Generate various waveforms.

Block Name	Purpose (Continued)
Sine Wave	Generate a sine wave.
Step	Generate a step function.
Uniform Random Number	Generate uniformly distributed random numbers.

User-Defined Functions

The *User-Defined Functions* library contains blocks that allow you to define the function that relates inputs to outputs.

Block Name	Purpose
Fcn	Apply a specified expression to the input.
MATLAB Fcn	Apply a MATLAB function or expression to the input.
S-Function	Access an S-function.
S-Function Builder	Builds a C MEX S-function from specifications and code that you supply.

Blocksets and Toolboxes

The *Blocksets and Toolboxes* library contains the Extras block library of specialized blocks.

Demos Library

The *Demos* library contains useful MATLAB and Simulink demos.

Index

A

Abs block
    zero crossings 3-17
absolute tolerance
    definition 8-12
    simulation accuracy 8-40
Action Port block
    in subsystem 5-38
Adams-Bashforth-Moulton PECE solver 8-9
algebraic loops
    direct feedthrough blocks 3-18
    displaying 3-22
    highlighting 11-24
    identifying blocks in 11-21
    simulation speed 8-40
aligning blocks 6-5
annotations
    changing font 5-16
    creating 5-16
    definition 5-16
    deleting 5-16
    editing 5-16
    moving 5-16
    using symbols and Greek letters in 5-17
    using TeX formatting commands in 5-17
Apply button on Mask Editor 10-13
Assignment block
    and For Iterator block 5-42
Assignment mask parameter 10-18
attributes format string 5-15
AttributesFormatString block parameter 6-11
Autoscale icon drawing coordinates 10-16

B

Backlash block
    zero crossings 3-17

backpropagating sample time 3-30
Backspace key
    deleting annotations 5-16
    deleting blocks 6-6
    deleting labels 7-15
Band-Limited White Noise block
    simulation speed 8-40
block
    finding specific 1-8
block callback parameters 5-50
Block data tips 6-2
block descriptions
    creating 10-8
block diagrams
    printing 4-12
block icons
    displaying execution order on 6-17
block indexes
    debugger 11-6
block libraries
    adding to Library Browser 6-33
    Blocksets and Toolboxes A-19
    definition 6-25
    Demos A-20
    Extras A-19
    searching 6-33
block names
    changing location 6-14
    copied blocks 6-4
    editing 6-14
    flipping location 6-14
    generated for copied blocks 6-5
    hiding and showing 6-15
    location 6-13
    rules 6-13